New Junior Cycle

Music

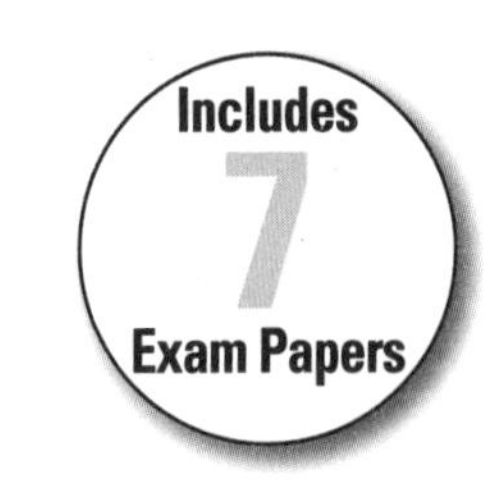

Contents

Revision Essentials

Teacher's Listening CD Track Listings and Student Edco Audio App

Tracks 1-1 - 1-24	SEC 2022 Exam Paper
Tracks 1-25 - 1-41	SEC Sample Paper
Tracks 2-1 - 2-12	Edco Sample A
Tracks 2-13 - 2-24	Edco Sample B
Tracks 2-25 - 2-36	Edco Sample C
Tracks 2-37 - 2-47	Edco Sample D
Tracks 2-48 - 2-60	Edco Sample E
Tracks 2-61 - 2-74	Practical rhythm, melody and sight clapping tests

Essential Guide

Junior Cycle Music

Marks 400 total (Practical 120 marks + Written paper 280 marks)

As part of the Junior Cycle Music course, students must complete two classroom-based assessments (CBAs), one performance exam (in March or April) and sit a 1 hour 30 minute common level written exam at the end of third year. The written examination will be linked to the 36 Learning Outcomes for final assessment (see pages v–vii) and should reflect your learning experiences during your learning journey, from first to third year, as a music student.

How Is Coursework Assessed for Junior Cycle Music?

The grid below outlines how students will be assessed over the course of their junior cycle learning journey.

Assessment has four components:

Component	What?	When?	Marks and Percentage
1. Classroom-Based Assessment 1	Compositional Portfolio	2nd year	Descriptor on JCPA
2. Classroom-Based Assessment 2	Programme Note (relating to Practical exam)	3rd year **in advance of Practical exam**	Descriptor on JCPA
3. Practical Exam	Perform 3 pieces and complete one unprepared test	3rd year **March/April**	30% 120 Marks
4. Written Exam	1 hour 30 minute written paper	3rd year **June**	70% 280 marks

General Advice

Classroom-Based Assessment Two: The Programme Note

The Composition Portfolio (CBA1) is completed in second year. In third year you will complete, **a Programme Note (CBA2)** in the weeks leading up to your Practical Exam. Your Programme Note provides information about the pieces you are preparing for your Practical Exam. A Programme Note should inform the audience about the music they will hear during your practical performance.

The descriptor awarded for both CBAs is printed on your Junior Cycle Profile of Achievement (JCPA) as a record of your learning over the three years of Junior Cycle. CBA2 is linked to your practical exam which takes place in March or April. Supports to assist you in completing CBA2 can be found in the Practical and Unprepared Tests section of this set of papers.

Practical and Written Exam

Both the Practical Exam and final Written Exam are set and marked by the State Examinations Commission (SEC).

Practical Exam

The practical exam consists of a performance of three songs/pieces chosen by you. Songs and pieces can be presented on a variety of instruments or through a combination of voice and instruments. Solo and group performance can be freely mixed. You must also complete

one unprepared test. The duration of the practical exam is **15 minutes**.

Performing: You can choose to perform your songs/pieces on a variety of different instruments and you can decide to perform as a soloist or as part of a group/ensemble for each piece. You can perform to a live accompaniment or use a recording, provided **the part or line that you are performing is not heard on the backing track** you have chosen. Mobile phones cannot be used to play your backing track, nor can tracks be downloaded or streamed live from the internet during the exam. **Backing tracks must be in hard copy on CD/DVD/USB/computer hard drive.**

Unprepared tests: You can choose **one** from the following options; (i) aural memory (rhythmic or melodic), (ii) sight reading (instrumental/vocal/rhythmic) or (iii) improvisation. **All tests will be four bars long.**

- Aural memory tests will he heard three times; you attempt the test after the second and third playing and marks are awarded for the best attempt.
- When sight reading, you will have a minute to look at your tests and one attempt only at performing it. Rhythmic sight reading can be clapped, tapped or played on an unpitched percussion instrument.

Further supports and information on your Practical Exam is provided in the Practical and Unprepared Tests section of this set of papers. Supplementary supports have been designed to help you prepare for the Unprepared Tests which are worth **20% (24 marks)** of the Practical grade. Audio tracks for Aural Memory tests and Sight-Reading samples are included in this section of the papers. Engage with these as often as you can to help you prepare for this part of your exam.

Written Exam

The music exam is a common level paper and carries 280 marks. In any given year, a selection of Learning Outcomes will be assessed. **There are six questions on the exam paper.** There are audio excerpts for each question. Answering time will be indicated for each question on the CD.

You have **1 hour 30 minutes** to complete your answer booklet. You are required to answer **all** six questions on the paper. Read the questions carefully. Insert answers in the spaces provided within the boundary boxes on each page.

There is a test excerpt at the beginning of your exam. Listen carefully to this excerpt and ensure that all aspects of the track are audible and clear to you. You will need to inform the superintendent in the exam centre at this point if there are any problems with sound/CDs.

Your completed exam paper will be scanned for marking by your examiner. You must use **black or blue pen** only on the exam paper. **Pencil can be used for writing music notation.** Ensure you use a good quality pencil (2B) which can be seen and have a good quality eraser to use where needed. **NEVER write answers outside the boundary boxes on your exam paper** – anything written here will not be seen when your paper is scanned and you risk losing marks as the examiner will not award marks for answers or part of an answer which has been written outside of the boundary box.

Knowing what to expect in your written exam helps you to prepare for success! There will be six questions on your exam paper. Each question will have instructions at the beginning. Information on the number of excerpts and the number of times each excerpt will be played will be placed at the beginning of each question. Because there is no set format for the paper, you must read all instructions carefully. Do not move ahead of the CD or allow yourself to fall behind. Use the pauses allocated on the CD between each playing of an excerpt to read the questions and read over the answers you have given. Check that your answers are clearly presented and accurate. Answering time will be given for questions on the exam CD, helping you to plan your time when completing composing or other written questions where no music is heard.

Edco Sample Papers

Ensure that you take the time to complete each of the questions in each of the sample exam papers. Keep in mind that the style of questioning and the Learning Outcomes being examined will change from year to year. For this reason, we have included questions which focus on the 36 Learning Outcomes in the Music Specification. We have also included activities designed to support your learning and help you to continue developing your knowledge of music as you prepare for your written exam.

AUDIO FILE INSTRUCTIONS

SEC audio on the Teacher's CD and Edco Audio App reflects the sample examination, including all repeats and the number of times a track will be heard.

The Edco Sample Paper audio tracks supplied on the Teacher's CD and Edco Audio App are played only once with an indication on the Edco Sample Papers of how many times each track should be played/listened to when answering the question.

Learning Outcomes

Each of the 36 Learning Outcomes (LOs) on the Music Specification are listed below. Learning Outcomes identify the knowledge and the skills that you should acquire over three years of study.

Use the grid below to help with your revision. Track your learning by ticking the boxes next to each LO as you go. Use the Learning Links column to record additional information relating to your learning experiences for each LO; e.g. Key terms, names of pieces, composers or other helpful reminders which help to aid your revision for your exam.

LO No.	Learning Outcome	Learning Links
	Strand One: Procedural knowledge Creating and exploring *Students should be able to:*	
1.1 ☐	compose and perform or play back short musical phrases and support these phrases by creating rhythmic/melodic/harmonic ostinato to accompany them	
1.2 ☐	create and present a short piece, using instruments and/or other sounds in response to a stimulus	
1.3 ☐	design a harmonic or rhythmic accompaniment, record this accompaniment and improvise over this recording	
1.4 ☐	indicate chords that are suitable to provide harmonic support to a single melody line	
	Participating and music-making *Students should be able to:*	
1.5 ☐	read, interpret and play from symbolic representations of sounds	
1.6 ☐	listen to and transcribe rhythmic phrases of up to four bars and melodic phrases of up to two bars	
1.7 ☐	perform music at sight through playing, singing or clapping melodic and rhythmic phrases	
1.8 ☐	rehearse and perform pieces of music that use common structural devices and textures	
1.9 ☐	demonstrate an understanding of a range of metres and pulses through the use of body percussion or other means of movement	
	Appraising and responding *Students should be able to:*	
1.10 ☐	discuss the characteristics and defining features of contrasting styles of music represented in the local school or community	
1.11 ☐	illustrate the structure of a piece of music through a physical or visual representation	
1.12 ☐	indicate where chord changes occur in extracts from a selection of songs	
1.13 ☐	compare different interpretations or arrangements of a piece of Irish traditional or folk music, paying attention to musical elements and other influences	
1.14 ☐	compare pieces of music that are similar in period and style by different composers from different countries	

LO No.	Learning Outcome	Learning Links
	Strand Two: Innovate and ideate Creating and exploring *Students should be able to:*	
2.1 ☐	experiment and improvise with making different types of sounds on a sound source and notate a brief piece that incorporates the sounds by devising symbolic representations for these sounds	
2.2 ☐	create a musical statement (such as a rap or an advertising jingle) about a topical issue or current event and share with others the statement's purpose and development	
2.3 ☐	adapt excerpts/motifs/themes from an existing piece of music by changing its feel, style or underlying harmony	
	Participating and music-making *Students should be able to:*	
2.4 ☐	rehearse and present a song or brief instrumental piece; identify and discuss the performance skills and techniques that are necessary to interpret the music effectively	
2.5 ☐	prepare and rehearse a musical work for an ensemble focusing on co-operation and listening for balance and intonation; refine the interpretation by considering elements such as clarity, fluency, musical effect and style	
2.6 ☐	design a rhythmic or melodic ostinato and add layers of sound over the pattern as it repeats, varying the texture to create a mood piece to accompany a film clip or sequence of images	
2.7 ☐	create and present some musical ideas using instruments and/or found sounds to illustrate moods or feelings expressed in a poem, story or newspaper article	
	Appraising and responding *Students should be able to:*	
2.8 ☐	analyse the chordal structure of excerpts from a range of songs and compile a list of songs with similar chord structures and progressions	
2.9 ☐	distinguish between the sonorities, ranges and timbres of selections of instruments and voices; identify how these sounds are produced and propose their strengths and limitations in performance	
2.10 ☐	develop a set of criteria for evaluating a live or recorded performance; use these criteria to complete an in-depth review of a performance	
2.11 ☐	evaluate the impact that technology is having on how we access music; propose ways that their music, and that of their fellow students, can be shared to reach a global audience	

LO No.	Learning Outcome	Learning Links
	Strand Three: Culture and context Creating and exploring *Students should be able to:*	
3.1 ☐	collaborate with fellow students and peers to produce a playlist and a set of recordings to accompany a local historical event or community celebration	
3.2 ☐	examine and interpret the impact of music on the depiction of characters, their relationships and their emotions, as explored in instrumental music of different genres	
3.3 ☐	make a study of a particular contemporary or historical musical style; analyse its structures and use of musical devices, and describe the influence of other styles on it	
	Participating and music-making *Students should be able to:*	
3.4 ☐	compose and perform an original jingle or brief piece of music for use in a new advertisement for a product, and record the composition	
3.5 ☐	devise and perform examples of incidental music that could be used in a variety of contexts or environments	
	Appraising and responding *Students should be able to:*	
3.6 ☐	associate/match music excerpts to a variety of texts (words, film, language) and justify the reasons as to why this piece of music was chosen to match the text	
3.7 ☐	compare compositions by two or more Irish composers or songwriters; use listening, background reading and scores (where appropriate) to explain and describe differences and similarities in the compositions	
3.8 ☐	select a particular advertisement and analyse the role music plays in supporting the message and promoting the product	
3.9 ☐	investigate the influence of processing effects (e.g. distortion, reverb, compression) on the recording process; select some recordings and evaluate the use and effectiveness of such effects within them	
3.10 ☐	discuss the principles of music property rights and explain how this can impact on the sharing and publishing of music	
3.11 ☐	explore the time allocated to Irish artists and performers in a variety of local or national Irish media and present these findings to their class	

Practical Exam Tips

- Know what is involved.
- Be prepared for the Unprepared Test.
- Record your progress: Log your practice, ask for feedback and ask for help if you need it.
- Practice makes perfect: Practise – Record your performance – Listen back – Refine and repeat.
- Perform your programme of songs/pieces as often as you can, for friends or family too. The more familiar you become with your pieces, the less nervous you will feel on the day.
- Rehearse regularly with the accompaniment you intend to on the day of your exam and ensure that any backing tracks you may use fit the criteria set out in the Practical Exam guidelines.
- If you are performing with live accompaniment on the day, it is a good idea to record the accompanist's part so that you can practice with the recording, between rehearsals!
- If you are performing as part of a group, meet and rehearse regularly together.
- Familiarise yourself with the features of your pieces, such as the tempo and dynamic instructions for each song/piece.

General Advice for the Written Exam

Top Tips!

- Learn to focus on particular elements whilst listening: tempo, dynamics, texture, etc.
- Look for clues! Inspect sheet music to find clues such as rhythmic and melodic features.
- Consistently build your music vocabulary. Develop your fluency with musical terms, using these as much as you can when describing music.
- Read the question carefully, and pay attention to the specifics of the question.
- Take particular care when answering questions that invite you to describe, explain, compare or identify similarities and differences between excerpts.
- Familiarise yourself with the necessary time signatures and key signatures. A command of music theory is important when completing the theory aspects of the exam paper. Use the rough work spaces provided to brainstorm and refine your answers. Write clearly on the staves provided using a 2B pencil.

Exam Day Tips

- Arrive prepared. Blue or black pens only, a 2B pencil and a good eraser. Use blue or black pen when writing in the answer booklet. Pencil can be used for notation or staves and should be neat and visible for the examiner after the paper has been scanned.
- Read **all** instructions carefully.
- Listen carefully to the test excerpt at the beginning of the exam.
- Circle the number of times each excerpt will be played and place a tick next to it after each playing to help you keep track.
  - Excerpt 1, played (three) times ✓✓✓
- Remember you will need to answer **ALL** questions on the paper.
- Do not write in the margins of the booklet outside of the boundary boxes. If you need more space for your answer use the rough work pages in the exam booklet; taking great care to label the question correctly e.g.
  - Question 3(b)(ii) contd.
- Be careful to answer each question according to the instructions. There are many different styles of question: true or false, matching, multiple choice and longer written questions.
- Never provide more answers than have been requested.
  - E.g. Q3(b)(ii) Identify <u>two</u> instruments heard playing the <u>accompaniment</u> in this excerpt.
    - ❖ If you recognise more than two instruments playing the accompaniment, you may be tempted to give more than two answers to show this. Similarly, if you are unsure, you might be tempted to give more than two answers. Either way, the extra answers could cause you to lose marks! Only give the required number of answers even if you can identify more.
- Underline or highlight the important words in each question. This helps to focus your listening and your answers.
  - e.g. Name one <u>rhythmic feature</u> heard in this excerpt.
  - Name the <u>string instrument</u> playing the <u>melody</u> in this excerpt.

Music Vocabulary – Know Your Lingo!

Below is a selection of musical terms found on the 2022 and the SEC Sample papers. Check in with your understanding of these terms by revising and defining each of the terms in your copy as part of your revision. Developing a good understanding of the terms used in exam papers will help you build confidence with the music vocabulary found in them. This will help to focus your listening and develop your skill at identifying the correct answer to the questions asked.

You should repeat this exercise for each of the sample papers which follow the SEC Sample paper to continue to develop your awareness and understanding of the language used in the music exam papers.

2022 Exam Lingo!

- Soprano Voice
- Tenor Voice
- Block Chords
- Backbeats
- Ascending scales
- Descending scales
- Playlist
- Cadence
- Form
- Royalties
- Rallentando
- Incidental Music
- Fermata
- Trill
- Tremolo
- Pizzicato

Sample Paper Exam Lingo!

- Found Sounds
- Processing Effects
- Unitary
- Binary
- Form
- Rhythmic Feature
- Key note/Doh
- Texture
- Graphic Score Symbols
- Chord Changes
- Metronome
- Chord Progression
- Jingle
- Perfect Cadence
- Major
- Minor
- Tonality
- Pulse
- Music Industry
- Royalties

Sample A Exam Lingo:

Sample B Exam Lingo:

Map Your Progress!

JUNIOR CYCLE MUSIC	2022 SEC exam paper	SEC SAMPLE	Edco Sample A	Edco Sample B	Edco Sample C	Edco Sample D	Edco Sample E
Question							
1							
2							
3							
4							
5							
6							

Remember

- Answer all the questions on the paper.
- Use blue or black pens only in the answer booklet. Pencil can be used for notation or staves.
- Do not write outside the boundary boxes on your exam paper.
- Keep track of how many times an excerpt is played.
- Inspect sheet music to find clues such as tonality or rhythmic and melodic features.
- Label any work on rough work pages with care.

Study Hub

Your free online guide to smarter study.

Visit www.edco.ie/onlinestudyhub

New Junior Certificate Grading System

Percentage %	Grade Descriptor	Abbreviation *(what you will see on your JC profile of achievement)*
90–100	Distinction	DN
75–89	Higher Merit	HM
55–74	Merit	MT
40–54	Achieved	AC
20–39	Partially Achieved	PA
0–19	Not Graded	NG

2022. S41

2022J067C1EL

2022

Coimisiún na Scrúduithe Stáit
State Examinations Commission

Junior Cycle Final Examination 2022

Music

Common Level

Friday 17 June Morning 9:30 - 11:00

280 marks

Examination Number | | | | | |

Day and Month of Birth | | | | |

For example, 3rd February is entered as 0302

Centre Stamp

For Examiner Only	

For Examiner Only	
Total	
Grade	

Instructions

Write your examination number and date of birth in the boxes on the front cover.

There are **six** questions in this examination paper. Answer all questions.

- Write your answers in blue or black pen. You may use pencil for staff and graphic notation.
- Write your answers in the spaces provided in this booklet.
- Before the examination begins, listen carefully to the test excerpt. If you cannot hear the recording clearly, inform the Superintendent immediately.
- There will be suitable pauses throughout for you to read and answer questions.

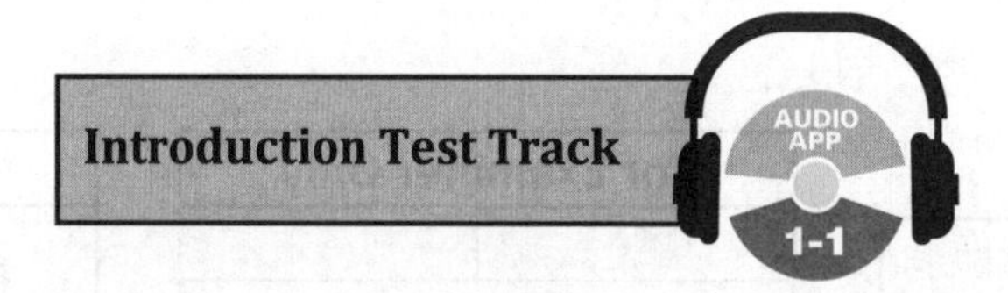

Question 1

(a) Excerpt 1, played three times.

Listen to the music in this excerpt and complete the following sentences. Choose your answers from the word bank provided.

Word Bank

handclaps	**soprano**	**guitar**
tenor	**piano**	**bass drums**

(i) The main melody is sung by a ____________ voice.

(ii) The __________ plays block chords.

(iii) There are _____________ on the backbeats (beats 2 and 4).

(b) Excerpt 2, played three times.

Select the feature performed by each of the following in this excerpt:

	Block chords	Ascending scales	Descending scales
(i) Backing vocals	☐	☐	☐
(ii) Piano	☐	☐	☐
(iii) Bass guitar	☐	☐	☐

This question continues on the next page.

(c) Excerpt 3, played three times.

Describe **one** feature of the music performed by each of the following in this excerpt.

(i) Lead guitar:

(ii) Bass guitar:

(iii) Vocals:

Roughwork

- You have five minutes to answer part **(d)**.

(d) The three songs in this question were collected as part of a playlist to welcome you to this exam paper.

(i) Name an event that you have created a playlist for.

Answer:

(ii) Name **one** song/piece, with its composer/performer, that you included in this playlist.

Song/Piece:
Composer/Performer:

(iii) State one reason why you chose this song/piece.

Answer:

(iv) Describe one way this playlist could be shared with a global audience.

Answer:

Do not write on this page

Question 2

(a) Identify the family of instruments performing the theme in each excerpt.

(i) Excerpt 1, played once only.

Woodwind	Brass	Percussion	Strings
☐	☐	☐	☐

(ii) Excerpt 2, played once only.

Woodwind	Brass	Percussion	Strings
☐	☐	☐	☐

(iii) Excerpt 3, played once only.

Woodwind	Brass	Percussion	Strings
☐	☐	☐	☐

(iv) Excerpt 4, played once only.

Woodwind	Brass	Percussion	Strings
☐	☐	☐	☐

This question continues on the next page.

Excerpt 5, played twice.

- Listen to the excerpt while following the score below.
- Answer the questions on the next page.

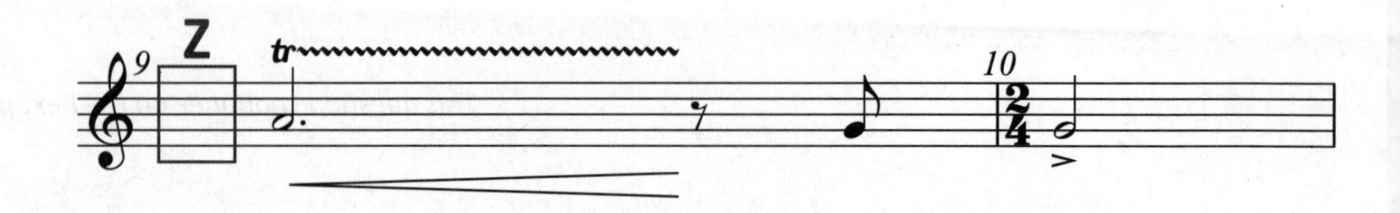

(b) Identify the **three** missing time signatures at **X, Y** and **Z** on the score.

	$\frac{2}{4}$	$\frac{3}{4}$	$\frac{4}{4}$	$\frac{5}{4}$
(i) **X**	☐	☐	☐	☐
(ii) **Y**	☐	☐	☐	☐
(iii) **Z**	☐	☐	☐	☐

This question continues on the next page.

- You have eight minutes to answer part **(c)**.

(c) Composing Task

Insert suitable chord symbols in the **six** empty boxes provided to add harmony to the Happy Birthday theme.

Happy Birthday

Patty & Mildred J. Hill

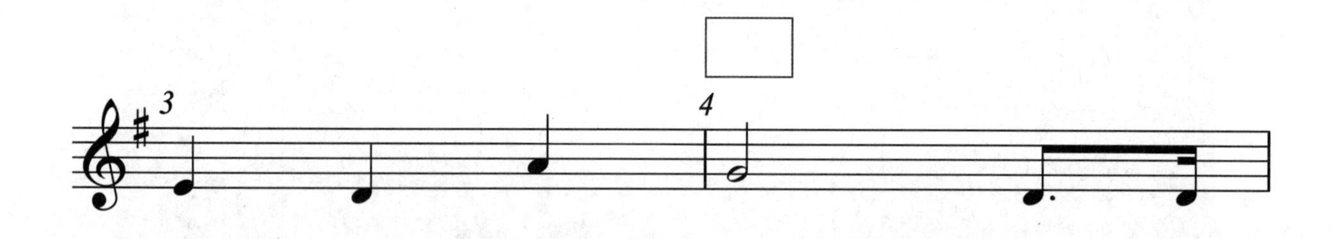

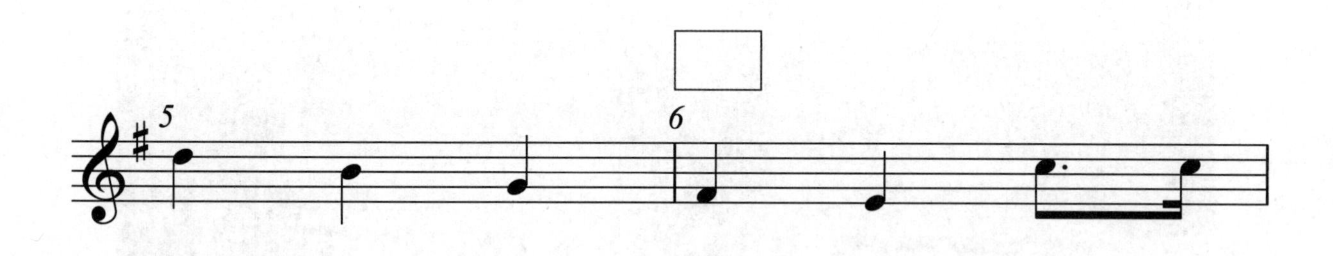

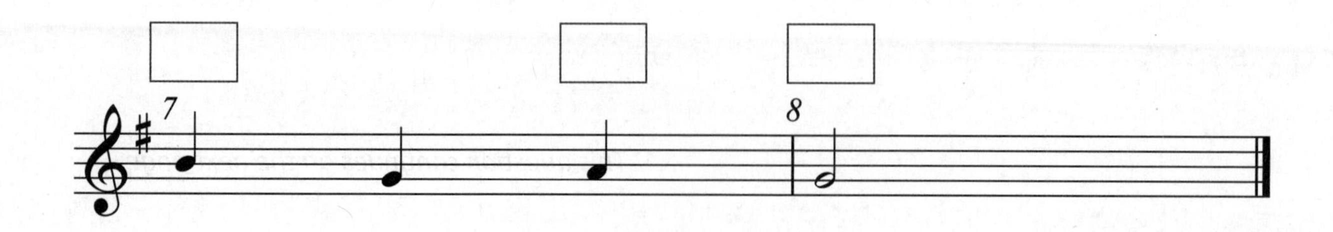

Chord bank grid – key of G major

Notes of chord	D B G	E C A	F♯ D B	G E C	A F♯ D	B G E	C A F♯
Chord symbol	G	Am	Bm	C	D	Em	F♯°
Roman numeral	I	ii	iii	IV	V	vi	vii°

Roughwork

Question 3

Excerpt 1, played three times.

- The lyrics are printed below.
- The boxes around the lyrics in lines 1, 2 and 4 show where the chords change.

(a) Insert boxes around **four** words in line 3 where you hear a chord change.

Line 1	By a **lonely** prison wall, I **heard** a young girl **call** - **ing**
Line 2	**Michael** they are **taking** you **away**
Line 3	You stole Trevelyan's corn, so the young might see the morn,
Line 4	Now the **prison** ship lies **waiting** in the **bay.**

Roughwork

AUDIO
APP
1-11

(b) Excerpt 2, played once only.

- Listen to the excerpt and answer the questions below.

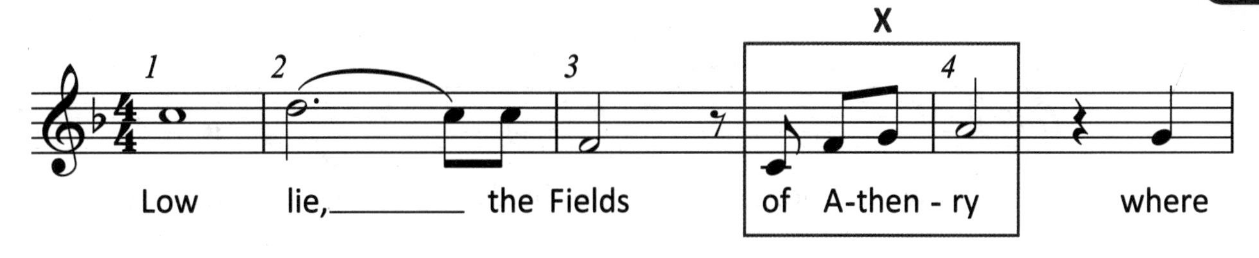
X
1
2
3
4
Low lie, the Fields of A-then - ry where

(i) Name the four notes at **X** on the score.

Note 1: ________	Note 2: ________	Note 3: ________	Note 4: ________

(ii) Three of these notes form the chord of:

C major ☐ F major ☐ G minor ☐

(iii) Name one note at **X** which is not part of the chord you chose in part **(ii)**.

Note name:

Roughwork

This question continues on the next page.

AUDIO APP
1-12

(c) Excerpt 3, played once only.

- Listen to the music in this excerpt and answer the questions on the next page.

Low lie, the Fields of A-then - ry where

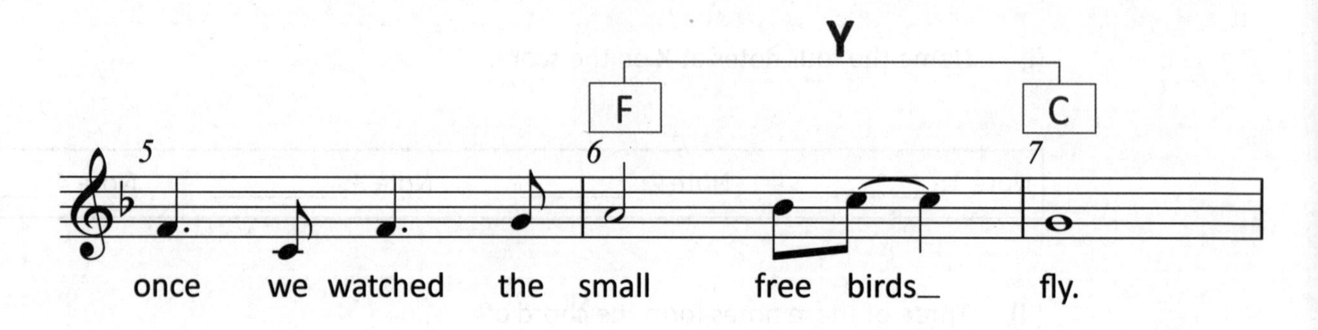
Y
F
C
once we watched the small free birds fly.

Our love was on the wing, we had

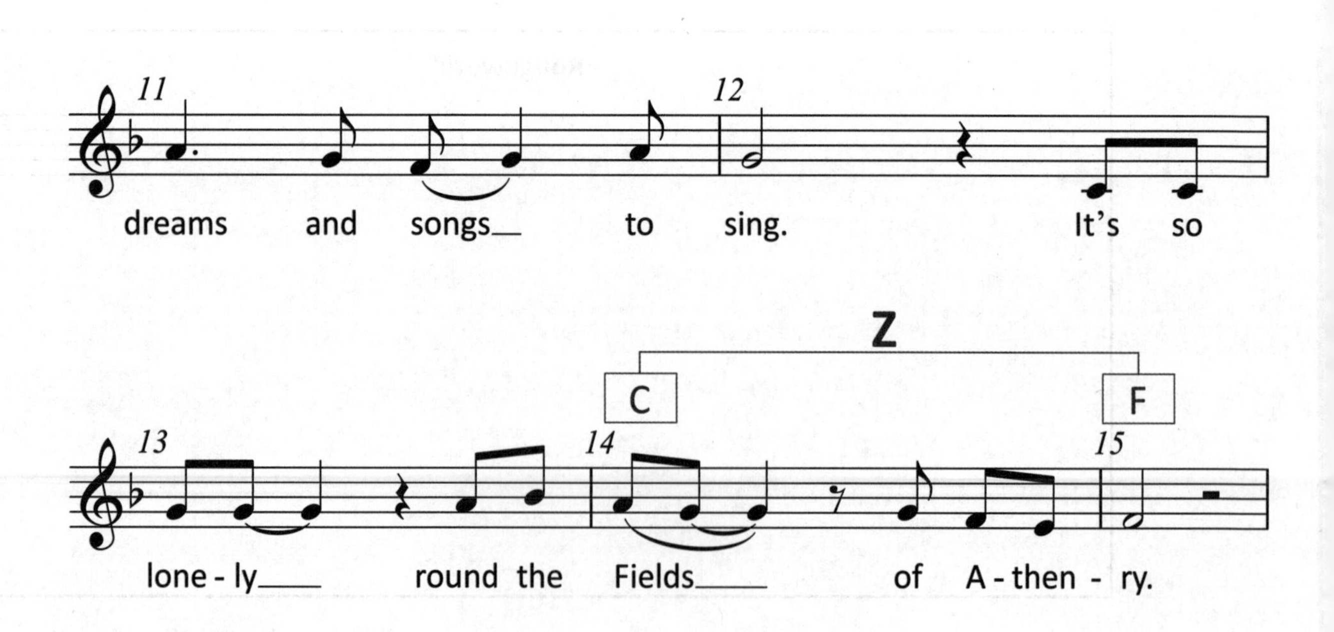
dreams and songs to sing. It's so
Z
C
F
lone - ly round the Fields of A - then - ry.

There are two cadences indicated on the score at **Y** and **Z**.

(i) Write the chord progression of each cadence in Roman Numerals.
A chord bank grid is given at the bottom of the page to help you.

(ii) Select the cadence that matches this chord progression.
A sample is given below to guide you.

	Chord Progression in Roman Numerals	Perfect Cadence	Plagal Cadence	Imperfect Cadence
Sample	IV – I	☐	✓	☐
Y	☐ – ☐	☐	☐	☐
Z	☐ – ☐	☐	☐	☐

Chord bank grid – key of F major

Chord symbol	F	Gm	Am	B♭	C	Dm	E°
Roman numeral	I	ii	iii	IV	V	vi	vii°

Roughwork

This question continues on the next page.

(d) Excerpt 4, played three times.

- The lyrics of the verse are shown below. The shape of the melody for lines 1 and 2 is represented by graphics.

Line 1 In Oranmore, the County Galway

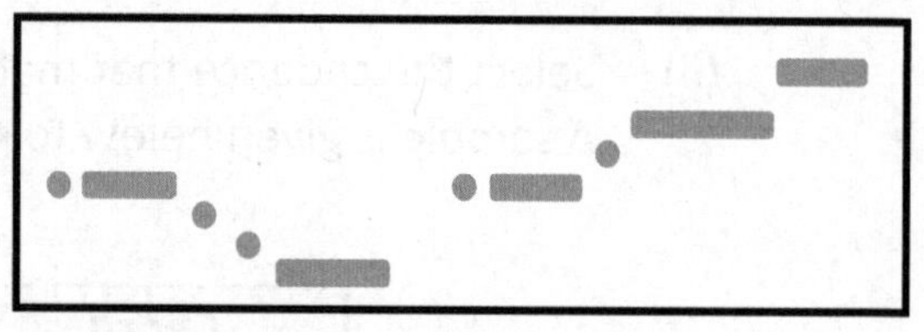

Line 2 One pleasant evening in the month of May

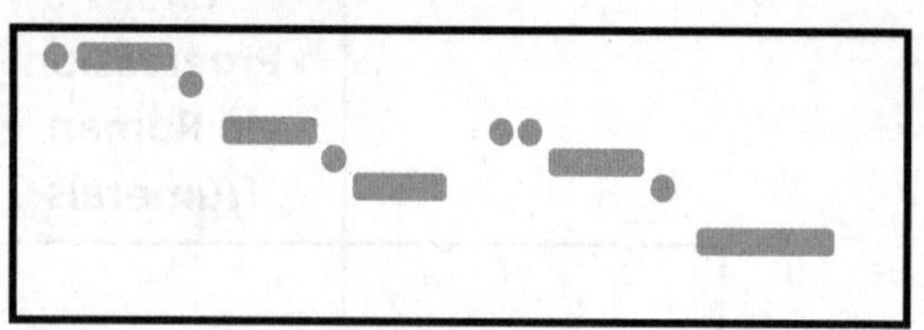

Line 3 I spied a cailín, both rare and handsome,

Line 4 And her beauty fairly took my breath away.

(i) Select the graphic which best represents the melody in line 3.

☐ 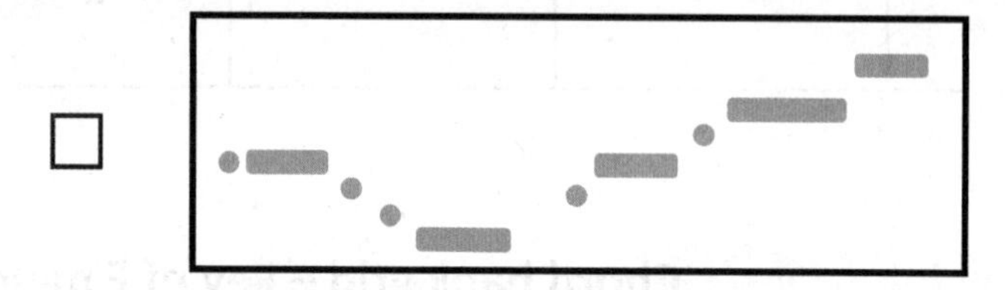

☐ 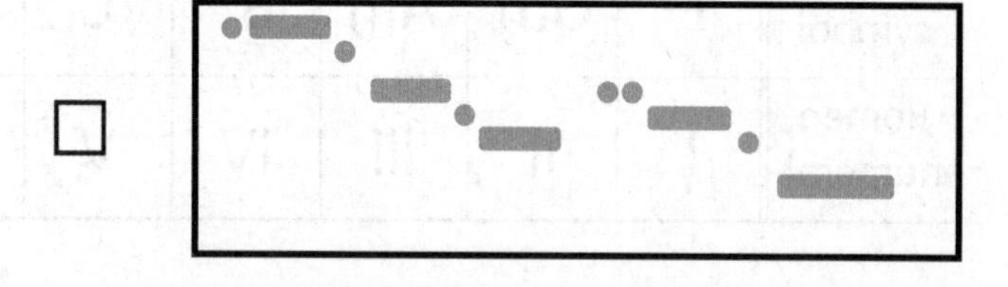

☐ 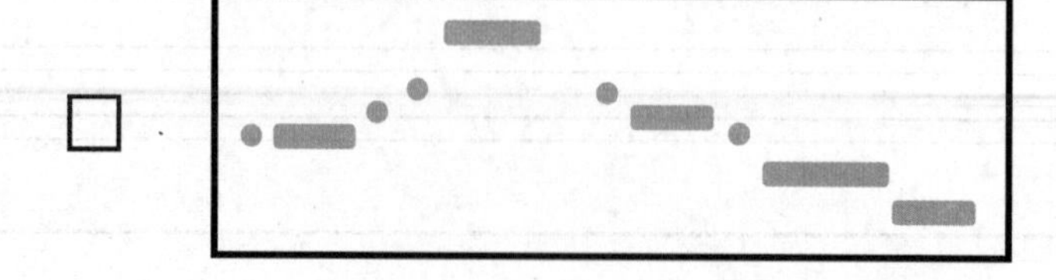

(ii) The form of this song is:

ABAB	ABBA	ABAA
☐	☐	☐

(iii) This form is known as:

unitary	binary	ternary
☐	☐	☐

Roughwork

This question continues on the next page.

Excerpt 5 and **Excerpt 6, played twice.**

(e) With reference to musical features, describe **one** similarity and **one** difference between **Excerpt 5** and **Excerpt 6**.

(i) Similarity:

(ii) Difference:

Roughwork

2022

- You have five minutes to answer part **(f)**.

(f) All of the songs in this question were performed by Irish songwriters, artists and ensembles.

(i) Describe one way in which the music of Irish performers is promoted on local or national Irish media.

Answer:

(ii) Explain one way in which Irish musicians benefit from royalties.

Answer:

(iii) Name one organisation responsible for collecting royalties on behalf of Irish songwriters and performers.

Answer:

Question 4

Excerpt 1

Excerpt 2

Excerpt 3

(a) Three excerpts, played twice.

(i) Match each excerpt to one of the descriptions below.

(ii) Give a reason for your choice.

Excerpt 1

☐ **A:** Holiday in Ireland	☐ **B:** Dancing at a disco	☐ **C:** A calm moment

Reason:

Excerpt 2

☐ **A:** Holiday in Ireland	☐ **B:** Dancing at a disco	☐ **C:** A calm moment

Reason:

Excerpt 3

☐ **A:** Holiday in Ireland	☐ **B:** Dancing at a disco	☐ **C:** A calm moment

Reason:

This question continues on page 23.

Roughwork

- You have eight minutes to answer part **(b)**.

(b) Composing Task

Your school is running a jingle competition to promote the message of hand hygiene. One of your classmates has written lyrics and asked you to compose a melody.

(i) Compose your own melody in the key of F major to the given rhythm to complete the tune. End on the keynote/doh.

(ii) Add suitable phrasing.

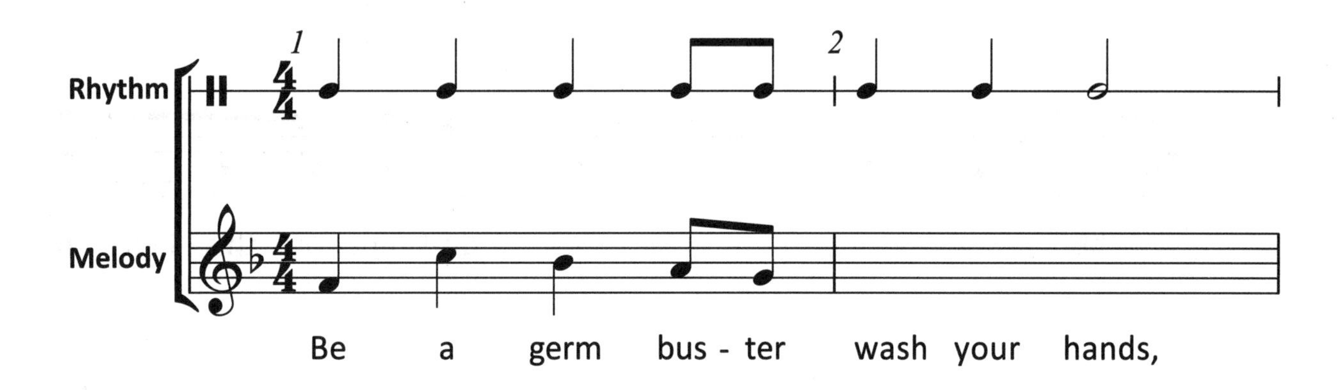

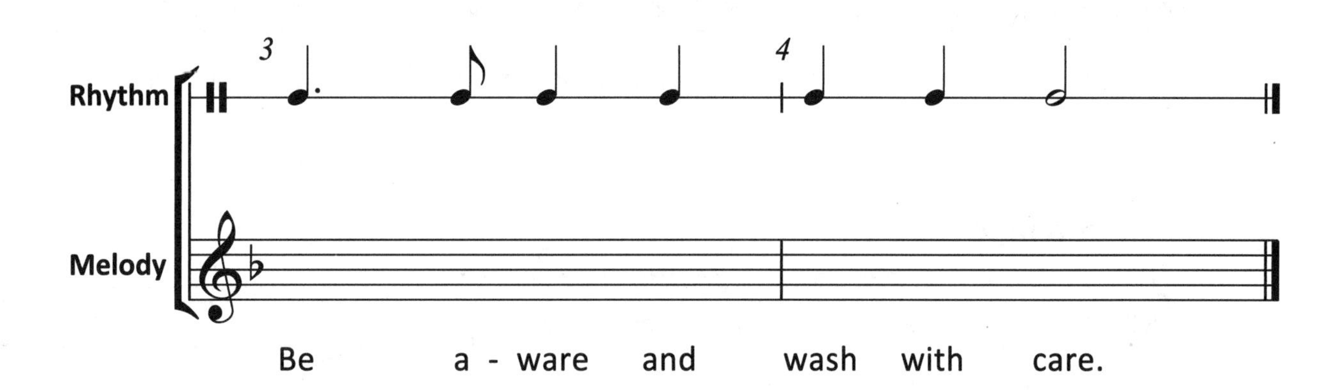

AUDIO APP
1-19

Question 5

Excerpt 1, played twice.

- Listen to the excerpt while following the score below.
- Answer the questions on the next page.

Andante
1
2
I had a dream my life would

3
4
be So dif-f'rent from this hell I'm

poco rall.
5
6
liv - ing So dif-f'rent now from what it seemed

A tempo
rall.
7
8
9
Now life has killed the dream I dream

Roughwork

(a) Identify the meaning of the following terms and symbols:

(i) 

This key signature indicates the key of:

- ☐ B-flat major
- ☐ F major
- ☐ D major

(ii) 

The dot after the note:

- ☐ adds half of the value of the note
- ☐ *staccato* (short and detached)
- ☐ *legato* (smoothly)

(iii) rall.

- ☐ gradually get quieter
- ☐ gradually speed up
- ☐ gradually slow down

(iv) 

The symbol above the note:

- ☐ fermata (pause)
- ☐ trill (ornament)
- ☐ *tenuto* (hold the note for its full value)

This question continues on the next page.

Excerpt 2, played three times.

(b) Fill in the **five** missing melody notes in bars 5 and 6 using the given rhythm.

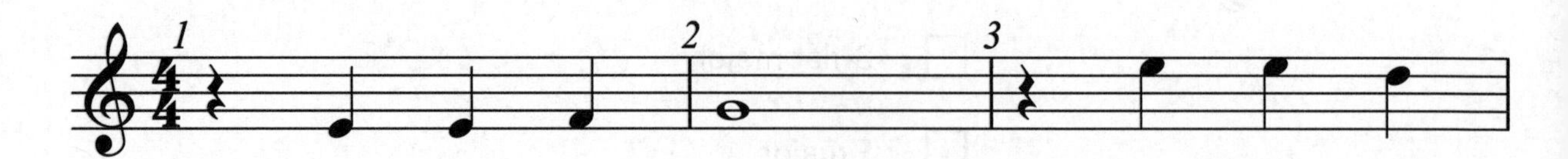

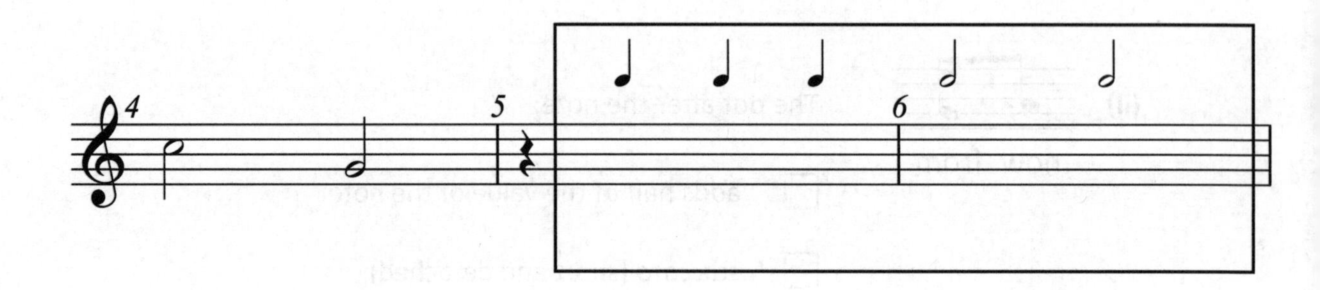

(c) Excerpt 3, played three times.

Describe the texture of the music in this excerpt.

Answer:

Question 6

(a) **Excerpt 1** – An excerpt from *Wasps* by Ralph Vaughan Williams played three times.

(i) Identify the feature played by **all** instruments at the beginning.

tremolo	trills	*pizzicato*
☐	☐	☐

(ii) Describe **one** other way in which the music represents a swarm of wasps in this excerpt.

Answer:

This question continues on the next page.

(b) **Excerpt 2** – An excerpt from the soundtrack to the film *Antz* by John Powell played three times.

The title of this music is *Antz Marching Band*. Describe **two** ways in which this performance could be refined with more rehearsal.

Answer 1:

Answer 2:

Roughwork

(c) **Excerpt 3** – An excerpt from *There's a bee in the car!* by Rupert Gregson-Williams played three times.

Describe **two** ways in which the music reflects the panic of finding a bee in your car.

Answer 1:

Answer 2:

Roughwork

This question continues on the next page.

- You have five minutes to answer part **(d)**.

(d) Each of the pieces heard earlier in this question could be described as incidental music.

(i) Explain the term *incidental music.*

Answer:

(ii) Describe a piece of incidental music you have created and performed.

Answer:

Do not write on this page

Do not write on this page

Junior Cycle Final Examination – Common Level

Music

Friday 17 June
Morning 9:30 - 11:00

2021J046C1ES

Coimisiún na Scrúduithe Stáit
State Examinations Commission

Junior Cycle Final Examination
Sample Paper

Music

Common Level

1 hour 30 minutes

280 marks

Examination Number

Day and Month of Birth

For example, 3rd February is entered as 0302

Centre Stamp

Instructions

Write your examination number and date of birth in the boxes on the front cover.

There are **six** questions in this examination paper. Answer all questions.

- Write your answers in blue or black pen. You may use pencil for staff and graphic notation.
- Write your answers in the spaces provided in this booklet.
- This examination booklet will be scanned and your work will be presented to an examiner on screen. Anything that you write outside of the answer areas may not be seen by the examiner.
- Before the examination begins, listen carefully to the test excerpt. If you cannot hear the recording clearly, inform the Superintendent immediately.
- There will be suitable pauses throughout for you to read and answer questions.

Do not write on this page

Question 1

(a) Four excerpts, played twice.

(i) Match each excerpt to one of the descriptions below. You may use each description once only.

Descriptions:
A. An enchanted forest
B. Soldiers marching
C. Alien invasion
D. The chase

AUDIO APP 1-25
Excerpt 1-4: first playing

AUDIO APP 1-26
Excerpts 1–4: second playing

(ii) Give a reason for your choice.

Excerpt 1.

Description: **A.** ☐ **B.** ☐ **C.** ☐ **D.** ☐

Reason:

Excerpt 2.

Description: **A.** ☐ **B.** ☐ **C.** ☐ **D.** ☐

Reason:

Excerpt 3.

Description: **A.** ☐ **B.** ☐ **C.** ☐ **D.** ☐

Reason:

Excerpt 4.

Description: **A.** ☐ **B.** ☐ **C.** ☐ **D.** ☐

Reason:

Roughwork:

(b) **Excerpt 5** – An excerpt from *I Did* by the Irish artist Bonzai played once. This is an example of music that uses found sounds.

- Read the following article and answer the questions that follow.

SEC SAMPLE 2020

HOW ELECTRONIC MUSICIANS ARE USING FOUND SOUND IN THE RECORDING STUDIO

> Me and John, the Producer, started hitting different parts of his metal desk with spoons and metal keys, which made that rhythm at the start.
>
> **Bonzai** – September 2016 (Adapted)

Found sounds are everyday sounds recorded by a composer to use in a piece of music. These can be environmental sounds, for example, the sound of wind whistling through the trees or rain pelting off a tin roof. They can also be human-made sounds, such as hand clapping or hitting a metal desk with spoons. Lots of interesting sounds can be blended into a piece of music.

After collecting their found sounds, composers then work in the studio with a recording engineer. They mix the found sounds and add processing effects such as distortion, reverb and compression to create their music.

(i) What are 'found sounds'?

Answer:

(ii) Name **one** example of each type of found sound below.

Environmental:
Human-made:

(iii) Name a recording you have studied and describe **one** processing effect used in that recording.

Recording:
Processing effect:

Roughwork:

SEC SAMPLE 2020

Question 2

Three excerpts from a version of the song *Isle of Hope, Isle of Tears*.

Excerpt 1, played three times.

(a) Listen to the music in this excerpt and complete the following sentences. The first letter of each word has been given to you.

(i) The opening melody is played on the c_______________.

(ii) Two bars later, the f______________ takes over the melody.

(iii) Both instruments belong to the w_______________ family.

(iv) The main accompanying instruments are members of the s____________ family.

AUDIO APP 1-28

Excerpt 2, played three times. The lyrics are printed below.

AUDIO APP 1-29

(b) Listen to the excerpt and answer the questions below.

Line 1	☆	On the first day of January, eighteen ninety-two,
Line 2		They opened Ellis Island and they let the people through.
Line 3		And the first to cross the threshold of that Isle of Hope and Tears,
Line 4		Was Annie Moore from Ireland who was all of fifteen years.

(i) Line 1 has a star beside it. Draw a star beside any other line that has the same melody as line 1.

(ii) Draw a different shape beside the remaining line(s) to illustrate the structure of the verse.

(iii) These shapes give the verse the form:

AABA ☐ AABB ☐ ABAB ☐

(iv) This form is known as:

Unitary ☐ Binary ☐ Ternary ☐

This question continues on the next page.

Excerpt 3, played three times.

(c) Listen to the excerpt and answer the following questions.

(i) Add stems and beams to the notes where appropriate to complete the rhythm at **A**.

'Isle of Hope, Isle of Tears'
Words and Music written by Brendan Graham

Excerpt 3, played twice more.

(ii) Name a rhythmic feature that you hear in the music.

Answer:

(iii) What are the letter-names of the three notes at **B**.

Note 1: __________	Note 2: __________	Note 3: __________

(iv) These notes form the triad of:

C major ☐ F major ☐ A minor ☐

(v) Why are there only three beats in the final bar at **C**?

Answer:

(d) **Excerpt 4 –** An excerpt from a different version of *Isle of Hope, Isle of Tears*, played twice.

AUDIO APP 1-31

(i) Identify **one** difference between this excerpt and **Excerpt 3**.

Answer:

Question 3

AUDIO APP
1-32

An excerpt, played four times.

(a) Bars 1–2: Fill in the **three** missing melody notes using the given rhythm.
(b) Bars 9–12: Compose your own melody in the key of B flat major to the given rhythm to complete the tune. End on the keynote/doh.

1
2
3
You are my Bel - fast love and there's no-one a -

4
5
6
bove you. You're my__ Bel - fast__ belle you see.__

7
8
9
There's no - one but__ you for me__ and___ I

10
11
12

'My Belfast Love'
Permission courtesy of Finbar Magee

Roughwork

SEC SAMPLE 2020

Question 4

(a) Two excerpts from *Copenhagen Steam Railway Galop* by Hans Christian Lumbye.

- Answer the questions below.

Excerpt 1, played three times.

(i) Which of the graphics below represents the shape of the first five melody notes?

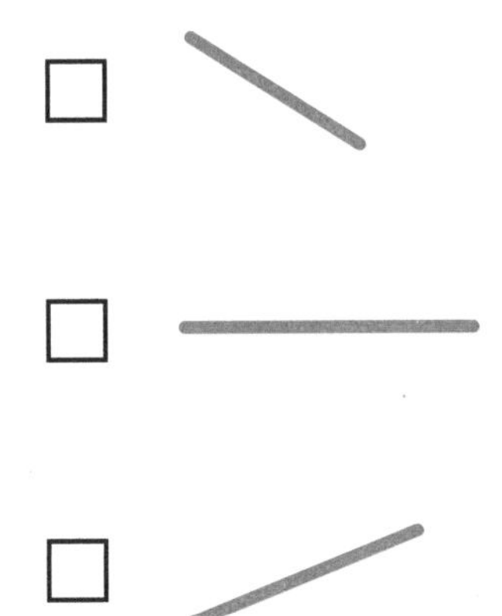

Excerpt 2, played three times.

(ii) Describe **one** way in which the composer represents the movement of the train in this excerpt.

Answer:

This question continues on the next page.

(b) **Excerpt 3** – An excerpt from *Motorbike Concerto* by Jan Sandström, played three times.

AUDIO APP 1-35

In this piece of music the trombone imitates the sound of the motorbike.

(i) Describe **one** feature of the music that helps to create the sound of the motorbike.

Answer:

(c) **Excerpt 4** – An excerpt from *Short Ride in a Fast Machine* by John Adams, played three times.

(i) Select the graphic that in your opinion best represents the texture of this excerpt.

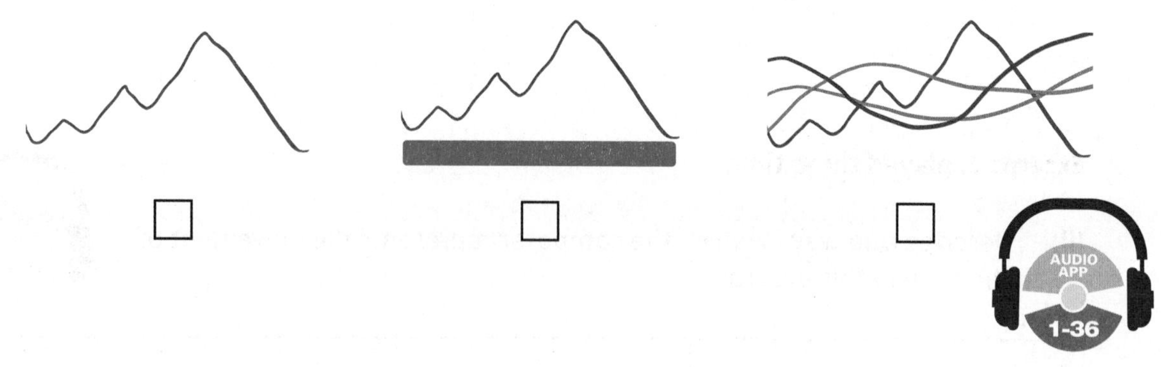

AUDIO APP 1-36

(ii) Give a reason for your choice of graphic, with reference to the music heard in the excerpt.

Answer:

(d) Composing Task

There is no music on the recording for this question.

Following a school trip to a funfair, you have decided to compose a piece called **Rollercoaster Ride**.

Using the table below:

(i) Name **two** different instruments or sound sources you want to use in your composition to reflect the rollercoaster ride.

(ii) Design a graphic notation symbol for each instrument to reflect the sound you want it to make.

(iii) In the case of each symbol, give clear instructions to the performer as to how to make the sound.

- A sample is given below to guide you.

(i) Instrument	(ii) Graphic Notation Symbol	(iii) Performance Instruction
Xylophone		Hit the beater against any note and *glissando* (slide) in the direction of the arrow. Thick arrows are played slowly and thin arrows are played quickly.

SEC SAMPLE 2020

Roughwork

Question 5

(a) Two excerpts, each played three times.

- Each of the numbered boxes represents one bar of the music, which is in $\frac{4}{4}$ time.
- Using the grid below, mark a ✓ in any bar where you hear a chord change.
- To help you, two bars of the pulse are given on the metronome before the start of each excerpt.

Excerpt 1, bars 1–8.

AUDIO APP 1-37

- The first two chords (bar 1 and bar 5) are given for you.

(i) There is **one** remaining chord change in this progression. Tick the bar where this occurs.

Bar No.	(Pulse)	(Pulse)	1	2	3	4	5	6	7	8
Chord Change	////	////	✓				✓			

Excerpt 2, bars 9–16.

- The first three chords (bar 9, bar 10 and bar 11) are given for you.

(ii) There are **three** remaining chord changes in this progression. Tick the bars where these occur.

Bar No.	(Pulse)	(Pulse)	9	10	11	12	13	14	15	16
Chord Change	////	////	✓	✓	✓					

This question continues on the next page.

(b) Composing task

A friend in Transition Year has asked you to add backing chords to a jingle melody to advertise their 'School Shop' mini-company. You will hear the jingle played once with the repeat.

Excerpt 3, once only.

(i) Insert suitable chords in the boxes provided. The final chord has been inserted for you. As the jingle is designed to be repeated over and over, it does not end with a perfect cadence.

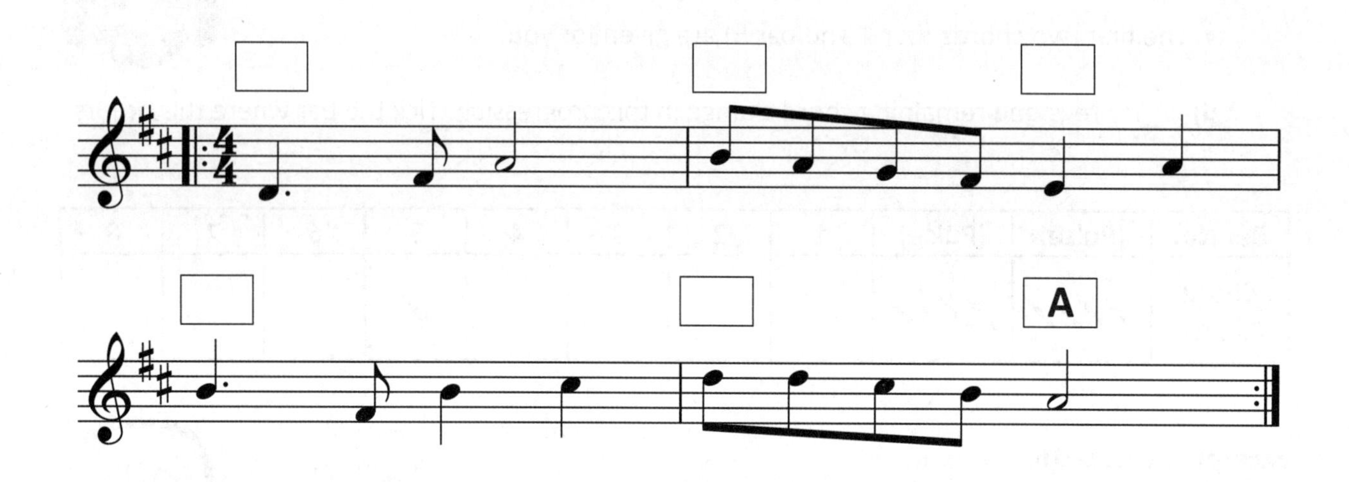

Chord bank grid – key of D major

Notes of chord	A F♯ D	B G E	C♯ A F♯	D B G	E C♯ A	F♯ D B	G E C♯
Chord symbol	D	Em	F♯m	G	A	Bm	C♯°
Roman numeral	I	ii	iii	IV	V	vi	vii°

(ii) Describe **one** other layer of sound that you would add to the jingle to vary the texture as it repeats.

Answer:

(iii) Explain how you would share the jingle with your school community to advertise the business.

Answer:

Question 6

Excerpts from two songs by Irish songwriters, each played twice.

- Answer the following questions.

(a) Excerpt 1.

(i) The instrument accompanying the vocals is the p_____________.

AUDIO APP 1-40

(ii) Describe **one** other feature of the music.

Answer:

(b) Excerpt 2.

AUDIO APP 1-41

(i) What is the tonality of the music?

Major	Minor
☐	☐

(ii) What is the pulse of the music?

3	4
☐	☐

(c) You will now hear both excerpts once more.

AUDIO APP 1-40 AUDIO APP 1-41

(i) Describe **two** differences between **Excerpt 1** and **Excerpt 2**.

1st difference:

2nd difference:

- You have seven minutes to answer (d) and (e).
- There is no music on the recording for these questions.

SEC SAMPLE 2020

(d) Composers and songwriters make their livelihood from their music. One way they do this is by earning royalties.

(i) Explain what royalties are in the music industry.

Answer:

(ii) How are royalties collected?

Answer:

(e) **(i)** Name a piece of music you have studied by an Irish composer or songwriter.

Name of composition/song:
Composer/songwriter:

(ii) Describe **one** musical feature of this composition or song.

Musical feature:

Do not write on this page

Junior Cycle Final Examination Sample Paper – Common Level

Music

1 hour 30 minutes

SAMPLE A

Junior Cycle Final Examination
Sample Paper A

Music

Common Level

1 hour 30 minutes

280 marks

Examination Number | | | | | |

Day and Month of Birth | | | | | For example, 3rd February is entered as 0302

Instructions

Write your examination number and date of birth in the boxes on the front cover.

There are six questions in this examination paper. Answer all questions.

- Write your answers in blue or black pen. You may use pencil for staff and graphic notation.
- Write your answers in the spaces provided in this booklet.
- Before the examination begins, listen carefully to the test excerpt. If you cannot hear the recording clearly, inform the Superintendent immediately. **An Example of this is on CD1 Track 1 and on the Edco Audio App.**
- There will be suitable pauses throughout for you to read and answer questions.

SAMPLE A

Do not write on this page

Question 1

One excerpt, played three times.

Listen to the music in this excerpt and complete the following sentences. Choose you answers from the bank provided.

Word Bank

Fast	**String Quartet**	**Orchestra**	**Slow**
Woodwind	**Homophonic**	**Strings**	**Brass**
Loud	**Percussion**	**Soft**	

AUDIO APP 2-1

(a) (i) Identify the type of ensemble heard in this excerpt ____________.

(ii) The dynamics in this excerpt are ____________.

(iii) The tempo of this excerpt is ____________.

(iv) B ____________ and w ____________ families play the melody.

(v) The accompaniment features instruments from the p ____________ family.

(vi) List two instruments which can be heard in this excerpt.

i
ii

(vii) Explain the term **timbre**.

(viii) Identify two instruments of the orchestra which have a **contrasting timbre** and describe how they differ in sound.

Instrument	Timbre
i	
ii	

(ix) Name **one** pitched percussion instrument.

(x) Explain the term **pizzicato** and name one instrument which uses this performing technique.

Description:
Instrument:

SAMPLE A

Four excerpts, played twice.

(b) Listen to each excerpt and answer the questions below.

Excerpt 1

(i) (a) The tonality of this excerpt is

	Major	Minor
Tonality	☐	☐

(b) Identify the texture of this excerpt

Excerpt 2

(ii) (a) The tonality of this excerpt is

	Major	Minor
Tonality	☐	☐

(b) Suggest a suitable tempo marking for this excerpt

Excerpt 3

(iii) (a) The tonality of this excerpt is

	Major	Minor
Tonality	☐	☐

(b) The melodic phrase heard in this excerpt sounds

Finished	Unfinished
☐	☐

Excerpt 4, played three times.

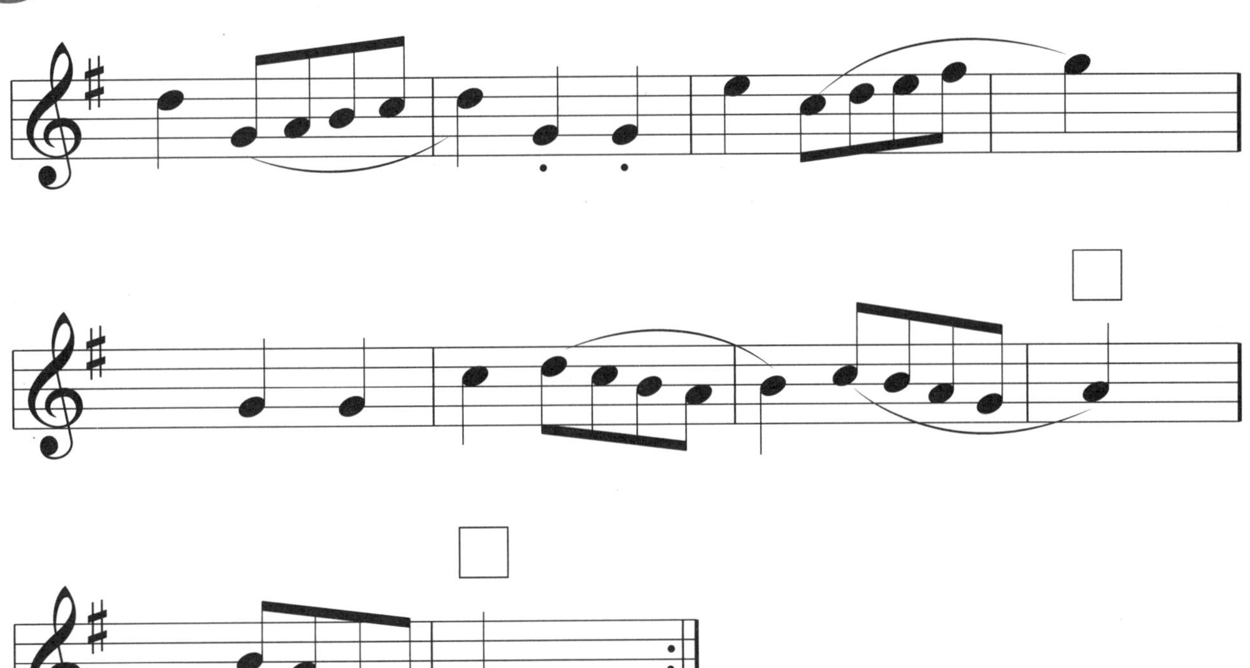

(iv) **(a)** Add suitable chords in the empty boxes provided to add harmony to the final bars of this phrase.

(b) The cadence heard in the final two bars of this excerpt is

	Perfect	**Plagal**
Cadence	☐	☐

(c) Name the two roman numerals used to create this cadence in the boxes provided.

Chord Bank Grid – Key of G major

Chord symbol	G	Am	Bm	C	D	Em	F♯°
Roman numeral	I	ii	iii	IV	V	vi	vii°

Roughwork

Question 2

Excerpt 5, played three times.

(a) (i) Listen to this excerpt and answer the questions.

(a) The melody is played by ______________.

(b) The tempo of the music heard in this excerpt is ______________.

(c) The time signature is $\frac{2}{4}$ ☐ $\frac{3}{4}$ ☐ $\frac{4}{4}$ ☐

(ii) Match the excerpt to one of the images below. Place a tick in the appropriate box.

A: Toddler Mealtimes! ☐ **B:** Dancing in the kitchen ☐ **C:** A Calm moment ☐

(iii) Give one reason for your choice.

(iv) Name **one** piece of illustrative music you have studied.

(v) Describe how a composer that you have studied has illustrated one of the following in a piece of music that you have listened to.

Characters	Mood	Emotions	Nature
☐	☐	☐	☐

(vi) Select **one** word below and describe **one** way this word could be illustrated in a piece of music.

sleeping ☐ jumping ☐ hiding ☐

Word:
Description

An excerpt from the opera *Lakmé* by Léo Délibes, played three times.

Listen to this excerpt and answer the questions.

(b) **(i)** The melody is performed by

Male voices	Female voices	Mixed voices
☐	☐	☐

(ii) Name the family of instruments that accompany the vocalists in this excerpt.

____

(iii) The texture of this excerpt is

Monophonic	Homophonic	Polyphonic
☐	☐	☐

(iv) British Airways is one of the UK's largest airlines. *Lakmé* is played at the boarding gates of their aircraft as passengers enter and leave.

Suggest **two** reasons why this music is a suitable choice for use on an aircraft.

Reason 1:	
Reason 2:	

There is no music on the recording for this question.

British Airways used 'The Flower Duet' from this opera in one of the airline's iconic TV commercials.

(c) **(i)** Select a particular advert that you have studied which uses music as part of the advertising campaign. Share the details of this advertisement in the space provided below.

Advert:

Product or Brand:

Music used:

Key message/theme:

(ii) Comment on the role music plays in supporting the advertising message and promoting the product. Refer to the music used and the product being promoted in your answer.

Question 3

One excerpt, played three times.

(a) Listen to an excerpt from 'Amazing Grace' and answer the questions.

(i) Identify the voice singing the melody.

Male	Female
☐	☐

(ii) Identify one instrument providing the accompaniment.

(iii) The tonality of the verse is

Major	Minor
☐	☐

(iv) The lyrics for this verse are printed below. The boxes around the lyrics in lines 1 and 2 show where the chords change. Insert boxes around two words in lines 3 or 4 where you can hear a chord change has occurred.

Line 1: Amazing **[Grace]**, how **[sweet]** the **[sound]**,

Line 2: That saved a wretch like **[me]**.

Line 3: I once was lost, but now I'm found,

Line 4: Was blind, but now I see.

SAMPLE A

(b) 'Amazing Grace' is performed in C major and uses the three major chords I, IV and V.

Chord Bank in C major

Chord symbol	C	Dm	Em	F	G	Am	B°
Roman numeral	I	ii	iii	IV	V	vi	vii°

(i) Identify the chord names of the progression I – IV – V. Write the names of the chords into the grid below.

I	IV	V
☐	☐	☐

(ii) List two other songs you have studied which use these three **major chords** I, IV and V.

i
ii

(iii) Name one minor chord that occurs in C major.

AUDIO APP 2-9

(c) (i) **Composing Task**

Insert suitable chord symbols in the 6 empty boxes provided to add harmony to this well known tune.

F ☐ ☐ ☐ ☐ ☐ C ☐

Rough work

Chord Bank in F major

Notes of chord	C A F	D B♭ G	E C A	F D B♭	G E C	A F D	B♭ G E
Chord symbol	F	Gm	Am	B♭	C	Dm	E°
Roman numeral	I	ii	iii	IV	V	vi	vii°

(ii) What style of accompaniment would you choose to play this chord progression?

Block Chords	Broken Chords	Sustained Notes
☐	☐	☐

Give one reason for your choice:

(iii) Name two instruments which are suited to playing the style of accompaniment you have chosen.

i
ii

(iv) Identify the **texture** of your completed arrangement of this musical phrase.

Monophonic	Homophonic	Polyphonic
☐	☐	☐

Give **one** reason for your answer.

Question 4

(a) (i) Explain the term **sound source**.

(ii) Identify two sound sources found in a classroom.

i
ii

(iii) Suggest a sound source which could be recorded to represent **one** of the following.

Thunder
Buzzing bees
Birds chirping

AUDIO APP 2-10

(iv) Listen to a reading of the poem by Roger McGough called 'The Sound Collector'. Select **two** words from the poem and describe one way in which you would use sounds to illustrate the two words you have selected.

word 1	Description
word 2	Description

'The Sound Collector' by Roger McGough from *You Tell Me* 1979, courtesy of United Agents

SAMPLE A

(b) (i) Explain the term **graphic score**.

(ii) Identify which of the symbolic representations match the motif heard in this excerpt. The excerpt will be played three times.

AUDIO APP 2-11

☐

☐

☐

(iii) Describe one way in which you have used symbols to notate music on a graphic score you created.

(iv) Give one reason a composer may choose to notate their music on a graphic score.

(v) **(a)** Design two symbols that could be used to represent sound in a graphic score called 'Beach Walks'. Insert the symbol below.

(b) For each symbol, name **one** sound source that you would use to create this sound and explain the reasons for this choice.

(c) Describe the instructions you would share with musicians in order for them to interpret the symbols you have chosen for your graphic score 'Beach Walks'.

Insert your answers to (a), (b) and (c) in the grid below.

SAMPLE A

Beach Walks

	Symbol 1	**Symbol 2**
Symbol	**(a)**	**(a)**
Instrument	**(b)**	**(b)**
Description	**(c)**	**(c)**

Roughwork:

Question 5

One excerpt, played three times.

AUDIO APP 2-12

(a) Listen to this excerpt and answer the questions.

(i) Identify the instrument playing.

(ii) Identify the processing effect used in this recording.

Panning	Distortion	Reverb
☐	☐	☐

(iii) Explain the term **processing effects**.

(iv) Identify **one** processing effect that you have studied. Describe the impact this effect has on a recording.

Processing effect:
Description:

SAMPLE A

(v) Identify a genre of music that uses one of the processing effects named in part (ii) of this question.

Genre:
Processing effect:

(vi) Name a piece of music you have studied which features processing effects.

(vii) Evaluate the impact that one processing effect, which features in this song, has on the recording.

Question 6

There is no music on the recording for this question.

(a) Identify **two** pieces of music that are similar in period and style, which have been composed by two different composers, from two different countries.

Period or style:		
Composer		
Country		
Piece of music		

(b) Make **two** comparisons between these two pieces of music from the period or style you have identified.

i
ii

SAMPLE A

(c) Which piece did you prefer and why?

SAMPLE B

Junior Cycle Final Examination
Sample Paper B

Music

Common Level

1 hour 30 minutes

280 marks

Examination Number					

Day and Month of Birth					For example, 3rd February is entered as 0302

Instructions

Write your examination number and date of birth in the boxes on the front cover.

There are six questions in this examination paper. Answer all questions.

- Write your answers in blue or black pen. You may use pencil for staff and graphic notation.
- Write your answers in the spaces provided in this booklet.
- Before the examination begins, listen carefully to the test excerpt. If you cannot hear the recording clearly, inform the Superintendent immediately. An Example of this is on CD1 Track 1 and on the Edco Audio App.
- There will be suitable pauses throughout for you to read and answer questions.

SAMPLE B

Do not write on this page

Question 1

Three excerpts, played three times.

This question features music from 'Galop Infernal' (better known as the 'Can Can') from *Orpheus in the Underworld* by Jacques Offenbach.

Excerpt 1, played three times.

Answer the questions by putting a tick (✓) in the correct box. Tick one box only for each question.

(a) **(i)** This excerpt is played by

Orchestra	String Quartet	Folk Group
☐	☐	☐

(ii) The melody is heard in the

Strings	Woodwind	Brass
☐	☐	☐

(iii) Name the percussion instrument heard playing on the offbeat.

Timpani	Triangle	Xylophone
☐	☐	☐

(iv) The opening melody is repeated and is

Exactly the same	Completely different	Almost the same
☐	☐	☐

Excerpt 2, played three times.

Answer the questions by putting a tick (✓) in the correct box. Tick one box only for each question.

(b) (i) There is a repeating melodic motif heard in this excerpt. The first four notes of this motif are

Descending ☐ Ascending ☐

(ii) How many times is the opening motif repeated?

2 ☐ 4 ☐ 5 ☐

(iii) Identify which of the graphics below represents the shape of the melodic motif heard in this excerpt.

☐ ☐

(iv) Name the family of instruments which play this melodic motif.

Strings	Woodwind	Brass	Percussion
☐	☐	☐	☐

(v) Name **one** percussion instrument heard in this excerpt.

SAMPLE B

Excerpt 3, played three times.

(c) (i) The time signature represents

two minim beats per bar ☐

two crotchet beats per bar ☐

two quaver beats per bar ☐

(ii) Identify **one** instrument heard playing the melody line.

(iii) Explain the use of ***ff*** below the first note of this melody.

(iv) An interval is the difference in pitch between two notes. Identify and circle the interval of an octave in the melody line printed in this question.

(v) Which of the following rhythm patterns is played by the cymbals in this excerpt.

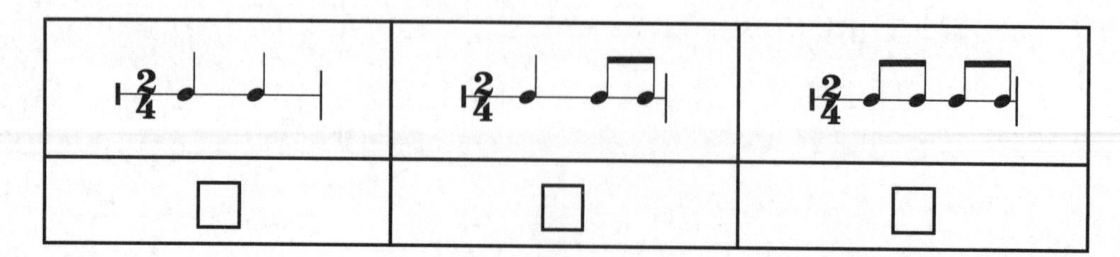

SAMPLE B

Do not write on this page

Question 2

One excerpt, played three times.

Excerpt 4

An excerpt from 'Tortoises' from *Carnival of the Animals* by Charles-Camille Saint-Saëns.

(a) **(i)** Insert the missing time signature on the stave.

(ii) Fill in the **five** missing melody notes using the given rhythm.

(iii) Identify the family of instruments playing the melody.

(iv) This is a piece of illustrative music. Explain the term **illustrative music**.

(v) Describe **one** way in which the composer illustrates the movement of the tortoise in this excerpt.

(viii) Describe **one** feature of the accompaniment.

Excerpt 3 (Can Can) and Excerpt 4 (Tortoises), played twice more.

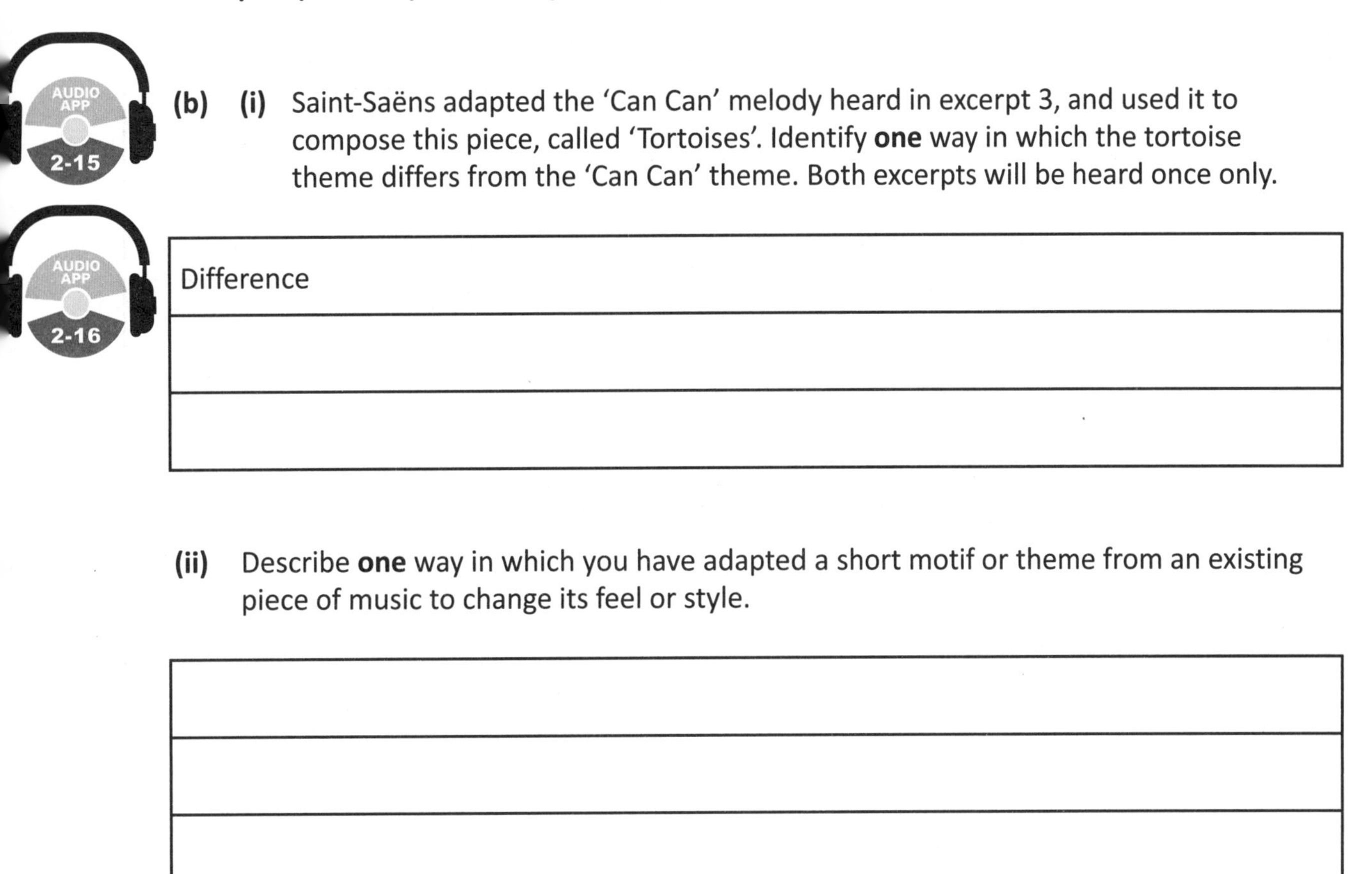

(b) **(i)** Saint-Saëns adapted the 'Can Can' melody heard in excerpt 3, and used it to compose this piece, called 'Tortoises'. Identify **one** way in which the tortoise theme differs from the 'Can Can' theme. Both excerpts will be heard once only.

Difference

(ii) Describe **one** way in which you have adapted a short motif or theme from an existing piece of music to change its feel or style.

SAMPLE B

Roughwork

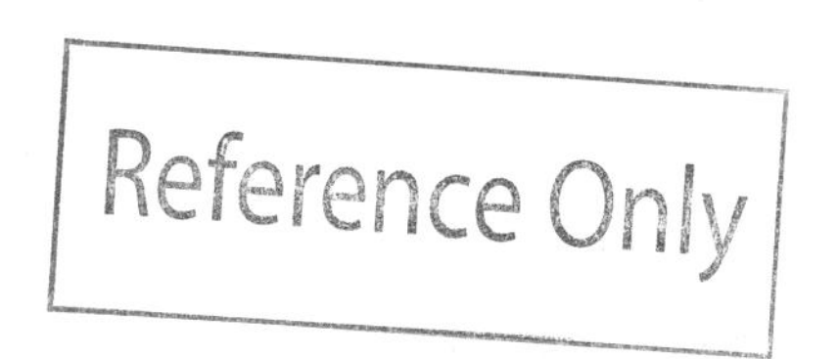

Question 3

Excerpt 1, played twice.

(a) In Excerpt 1 we listened to Offenbach's 'Can Can' from *Orpheus in the Underworld*. The melody below is taken from another work by Offenbach, the 'Bacarolle' from the opera *The Tales of Hoffmann*.

(i) Adapt the melody below by making **three** changes to it. Insert your adapted melody on the stave provided. A chord bank in C major has been provided for you.

Given phrase:

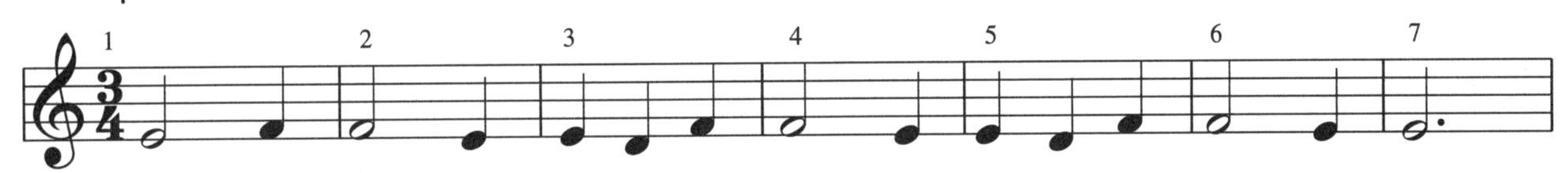

Insert your phrase here.

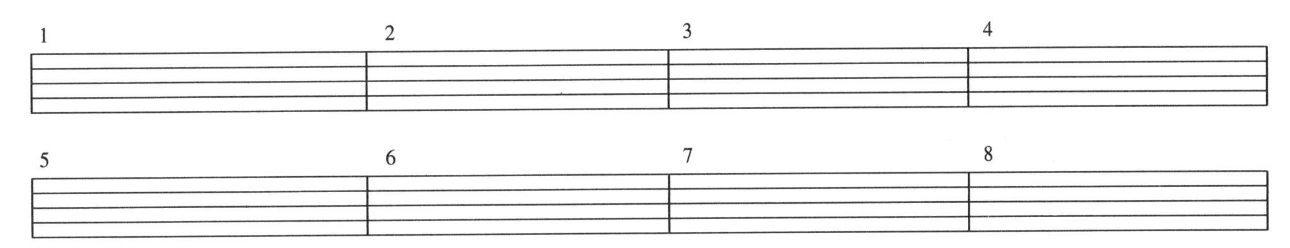

Chord Bank – C major

Notes of Chord	G E C	A F D	B G E	C A F	D B G	E C A	F D B
Chord symbol	C	Dm	Em	F	G	Am	B°
Roman numeral	I	ii	iii	IV	V	vi	vii°

(ii) Provide a brief description of **one** change that you have applied to the original phrase.

SAMPLE B

(iii) Composing Task

You have 8 minutes to complete part (iii)

Your school is running a jingle writing competition. You have been asked to compose the melody for your entry.

(i) Compose your own melody in the key of G major to the given rhythm to complete the melody. End on the keynote/doh.

(ii) Add suitable phrasing

(b) There is no music on the recording for this question.

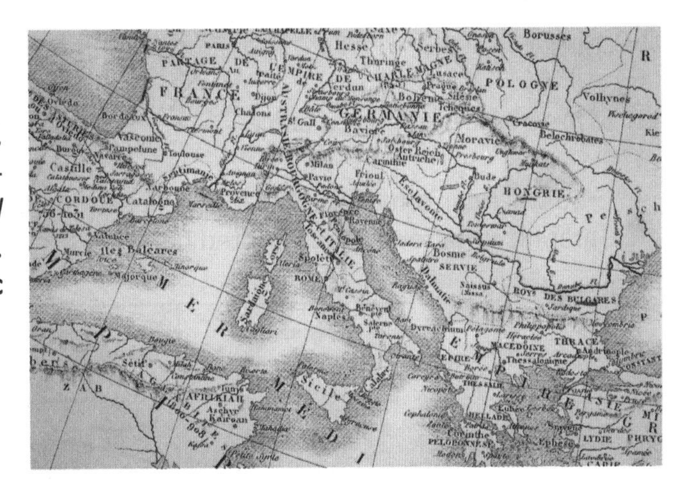

Jacques Offenbach, composer of 'Can Can', was born in **Germany** in 1819. Camille Saint-Saëns, composer of 'Tortoises' from *Carnival of the Animals*, was born in **France** in 1839. Both of these works belong to the **Romantic era**.

Write about **two** composers that you have studied who composed music in a similar period or style but **were from two different countries**. Describe **two** musical features of the style you have chosen.

Composer 1	Country:

Composer 2	Country:

Period/Style:

Musical feature 1:
Music feature 2:

Question 4

(a) Three excerpts, played twice.

You will hear three excerpts in this question. Identify which of the excerpts represents the graphic notation symbol printed below?

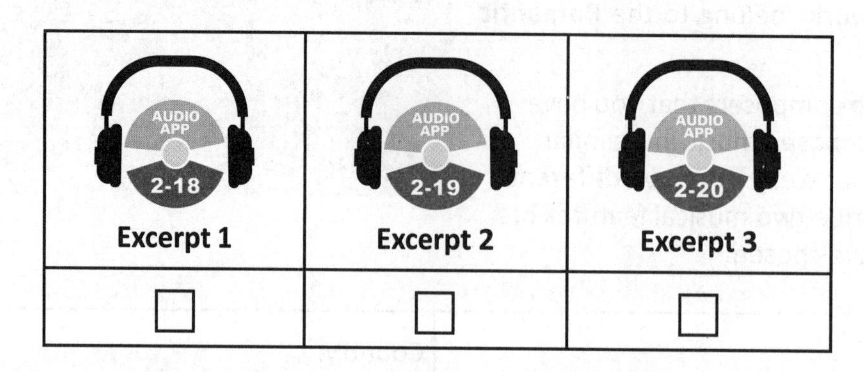

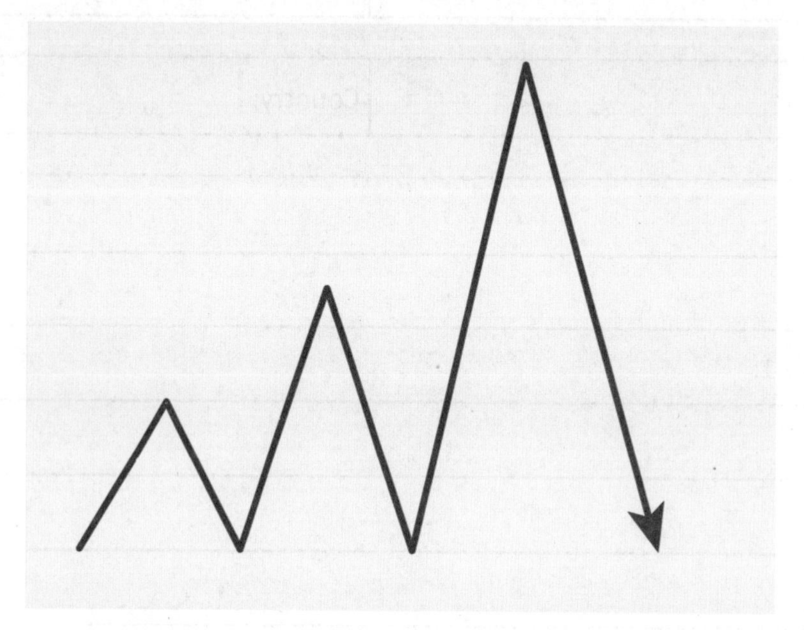

An excerpt played four times.

(b) You will hear a rhythm pattern played four times. Listen to the excerpt and identify the missing rhythm values. Insert the appropriate note values to complete the rhythmic phrase below.

Add the eight missing rhythm notes to the rhythm line below.

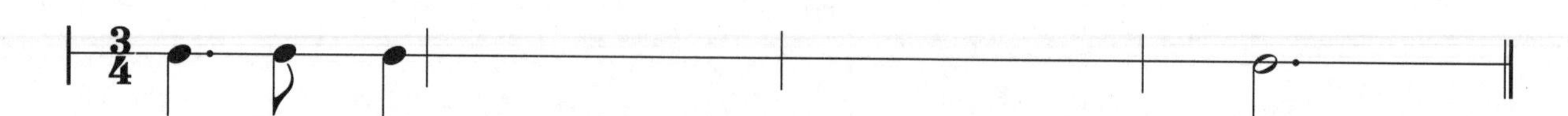

(c) There is no music on the recording for this question.

(i) Explain the term **jingle**.

(ii) Describe the role of jingles in advertising campaigns.

(iii) Choose **one** advertisement you have studied and explain how the music or jingle used in this advert helps to promote the product or brand being advertised.

Advertisement:	Product/Brand:

Describe the role music plays in supporting the message and promoting the product.

SAMPLE B

Question 5

(a) Three excerpts, played three times.

Excerpt 1, played three times.

The first verse of the folk song 'Scarborough Fair' will be played three times. Listen to this excerpt and answer the questions below.

(i) The vocalist singing the first verse is

Male	Female
☐	☐

(ii) Describe the tempo of this excerpt.

(iii) Identify the time signature heard in this song.

$\frac{3}{4}$	$\frac{4}{4}$	$\frac{6}{8}$
☐	☐	☐

(iv) How many bars of introduction are heard before the singer enters.

2	4	6
☐	☐	☐

(v) Describe one feature of the accompaniment in this excerpt.

(vi) The texture of this excerpt is

Monophonic	Homophonic	Polyphonic
☐	☐	☐

Excerpt 2, played three times.

The first phrase of this folk song will be played on piano.

(c) **(i)** Listen to this excerpt and **match** the melody notes to the lyrics.

(ii) Insert the melody notes you have selected on to the stave, taking care to align the notes with the lyrics correctly.

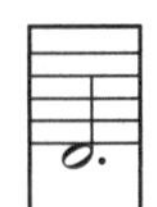

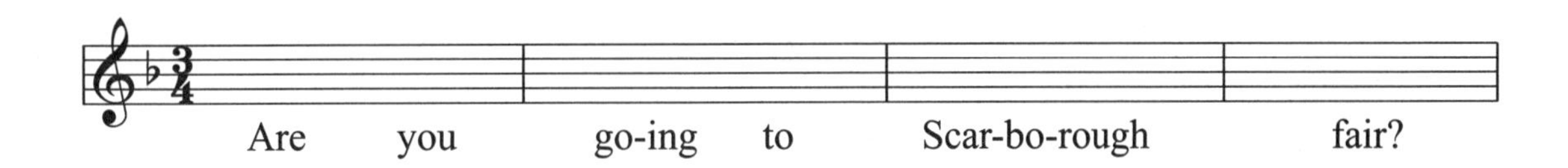

Excerpt three, played three times.

The third verse of 'Scarborough Fair' will be played.

(c) **(i)** What type of song is 'Scarborough Fair'?

(ii) Select the graphic that best represents the texture of this excerpt.

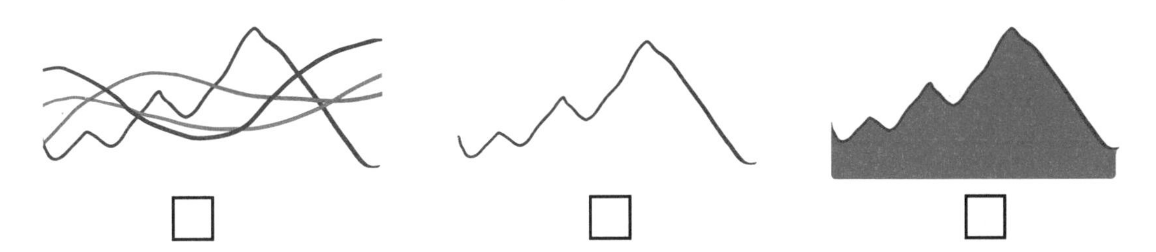

SAMPLE B

Excerpts 1 and 3 will be played once more.

AUDIO APP 2-22

AUDIO APP 2-24

(iii) Identify **one** similarity and **one** difference between verses 1 and 3.

(a) Similarity:

(b) Difference:

(iv) The tonality of this performance is

Major ☐ Minor ☐

(v) Other than the instruments heard in this excerpt, suggest **one** other instrument suited to accompanying this folk song.

(vi) Give **one** reason for your choice.

Question 6

There is no music on the recording for this question.

'Scarborough Fair' is an old English folk song. Many versions of this song exist; the most successful cover of this song recorded by Simon and Garfunkel in 1966.

Compare **two** different arrangements of a piece of traditional or folk music which you have studied.

Name of piece:

	Arrangement 1	Arrangement 2
Performer/s		

Do not write on this page

Junior Cycle Final Examination
Sample Paper C

Music

Common Level

SAMPLE C

1 hour 30 minutes

280 marks

Examination Number					

Day and Month of Birth					For example, 3rd February is entered as 0302

Instructions

Write your examination number and date of birth in the boxes on the front cover.

There are six questions in this examination paper. Answer all questions.

- Write your answers in blue or black pen. You may use pencil for staff and graphic notation.
- Write your answers in the spaces provided in this booklet.
- Before the examination begins, listen carefully to the test excerpt. If you cannot hear the recording clearly, inform the Superintendent immediately. An Example of this is on CD1 Track 1 and on the Edco Audio App.
- There will be suitable pauses throughout for you to read and answer questions.

SAMPLE C

Do not write on this page

Question 1

Excerpt 1, played three times.

(a) Listen to the music and answer the questions below.

(i) Name the instrument which plays the melody in this excerpt.

(ii) Identify **one** processing effect used in this recording.

(iii) Name a piece of music you have studied that uses processing effects.

(iv) Name **one** processing effect used in the recording you have named above.

Processing effect

Describe the effect this processing effect has on the recording.

(b) Three excerpts, played twice.

Excerpt 1

Excerpt 2

Excerpt 3

Listen to each excerpt and match the correct audio clip with the melody printed below.

Which of the following audio clips best matches the music printed above?

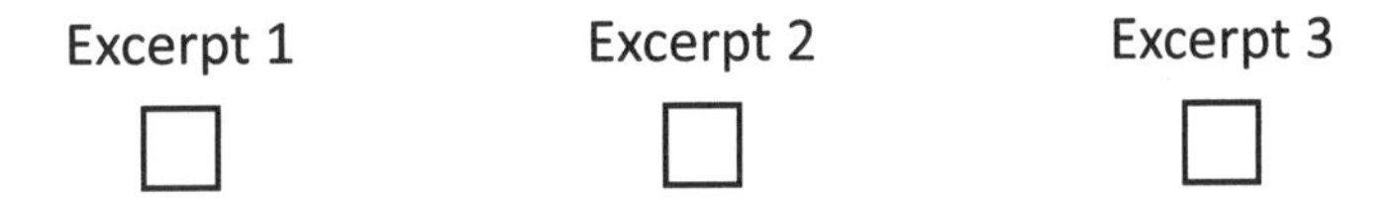

Excerpt 4, played four times.

(c) Listen to the music in this excerpt. Insert the **six** missing melody notes to complete the melodic phrase below.

Roughwork

Question 2

(a) Excerpt 1, played three times.

(i) Listen to the excerpt and identify the repeated rhythmic pattern heard in this excerpt.

☐	
☐	
☐	

(ii) Identify the time signature of the rhythmic pattern you have chosen.

$\frac{3}{4}$	$\frac{4}{4}$	$\frac{5}{4}$
☐	☐	☐

(iii) What musical term is used to describe the repeated rhythmic pattern heard in this excerpt.

(iv) Identify the instrument playing the rhythmic pattern heard in this excerpt.

Snare drum	Bass drum	Timpani
☐	☐	☐

(v) Suggest **one** other percussion instrument that could perform this motif.

(vi) Compose a two-bar rhythmic pattern in $\frac{3}{4}$ which could repeat whilst a guitar player improvises over it. Insert your two-bar pattern in the space below.

(b) Excerpt 2, played three times.

(i) Name the instrument which is now heard playing alongside the rhythmic pattern heard in excerpt 1.

(ii) In this excerpt the hi-hat is heard played on beat

1	2	3	4
☐	☐	☐	☐

(iii) Describe the texture of this excerpt.

(iv) Name the instrument which is introduced towards the end of this excerpt.

(v) Describe what this new instrument is playing.

Question 3

Two excerpts, played three times.

AUDIO APP
2-32

(a) Excerpt 1, played three times.

'Streets of London' is a ballad composed by Ralph McTell in 1969. Listen to this excerpt and answer the questions.

Have you seen_ the old man in the closed down mar- ket

(i) The introduction is heard played by

guitar ☐ violin ☐ harp ☐

(ii) The mood of the song is

Happy ☐ Sad ☐ Angry ☐

(iii) Identify the number of bars of introduction which are heard before the singer joins in the performance.

4 ☐ 6 ☐ 8 ☐

(iv) Identify **one** rhythmic feature of this verse.

(v) Identify **one** melodic feature of this verse.

(b) Excerpt 2, played three times.

The music for verse 2 is printed for you below. Listen to the music in this excerpt and answer the questions below.

Streets of London

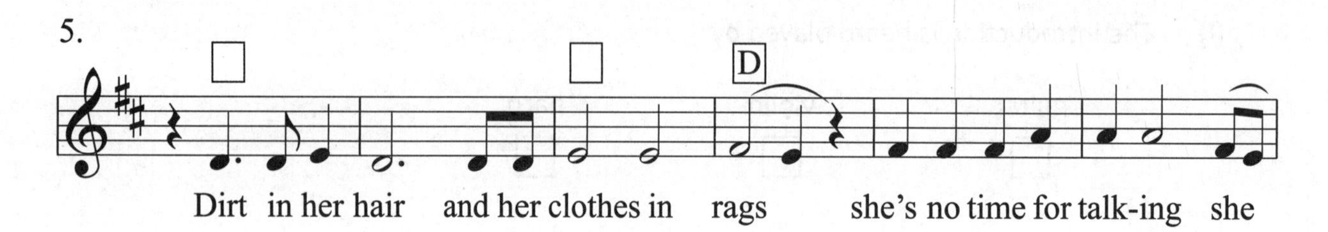

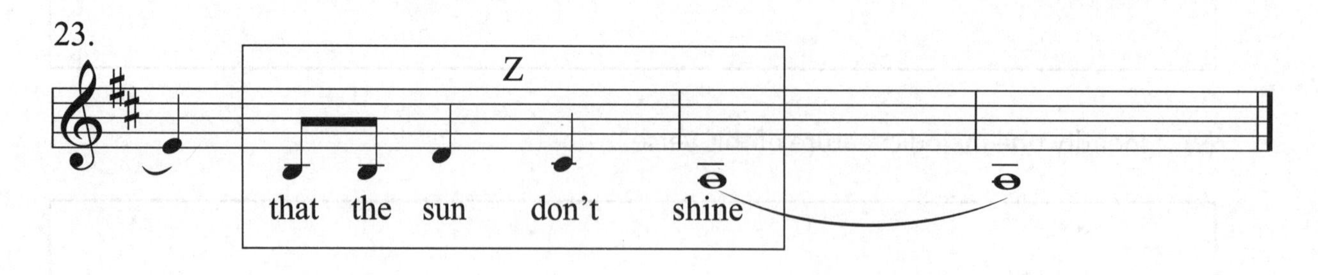

The excerpt will be played **once** only.

(i) Name and define the symbols marked **X** and **Y** on the score.

Name	**Definition**
X	
Y	

(ii) Name the **five** melody notes at **Z** on the score.

Note 1:________ Note 2:________ Note 3:________ Note 4:________ Note 5:________

(iii) **Range** is the number of pitches between the lowest note and the highest note in a piece of music. Circle the lowest pitched note and the highest note on the sheet music.

(iv) Identify **one** change which occurs from bar 17 onwards.

(v) You have been asked to add backing chords to the opening two phrases of this song for a guitar player in your class to accompany you in your practical.

Insert suitable chords in the boxes provided on the score. The final chord has been inserted for you. A chord bank has been provided for you below.

Chord Bank – D major

Notes of chord	A F♯ D	B G E	C♯ A F♯	D B G	E C♯ A	F♯ D B	G E C♯
Chord symbol	D	Em	F♯m	G	A	Bm	C♯°
Roman numeral	I	ii	iii	IV	V	vi	vii°

SAMPLE C

Question 4

Three excerpts, played three times.

(a) In this question you will hear **three excerpts** from *Romeo and Juliet* Suite No. 2 'Montagues and the Capulets' by Sergei Prokofiev. This work is also known as the 'Dance of the Knights'.

Excerpt 1, played three times

Answer the questions by putting a tick (✓) in the correct box. Tick one box only for each question.

(i) The pulsing notes heard in the opening bars are played by

strings and woodwind	strings and brass	brass and woodwind
☐	☐	☐

(ii) Identify the family of instruments which play the melody in this excerpt.

woodwind	brass	strings
☐	☐	☐

(iii) The tonality of this section is

major	minor
☐	☐

(iv) The time sigature is

$\genfrac{}{}{0pt}{}{3}{4}$	$\genfrac{}{}{0pt}{}{4}{4}$	$\genfrac{}{}{0pt}{}{6}{8}$
☐	☐	☐

(v) Identify **one** feature of the melody.

(vi) Identify the mood of this section.

calm	cheerful	tense
☐	☐	☐

Describe **one** feature of the music which helps to illustrate the mood you have selected.

(vii) The texture is

monophonic	homophonic	polyphonic
☐	☐	☐

Give **one** reason for your choice of texture.

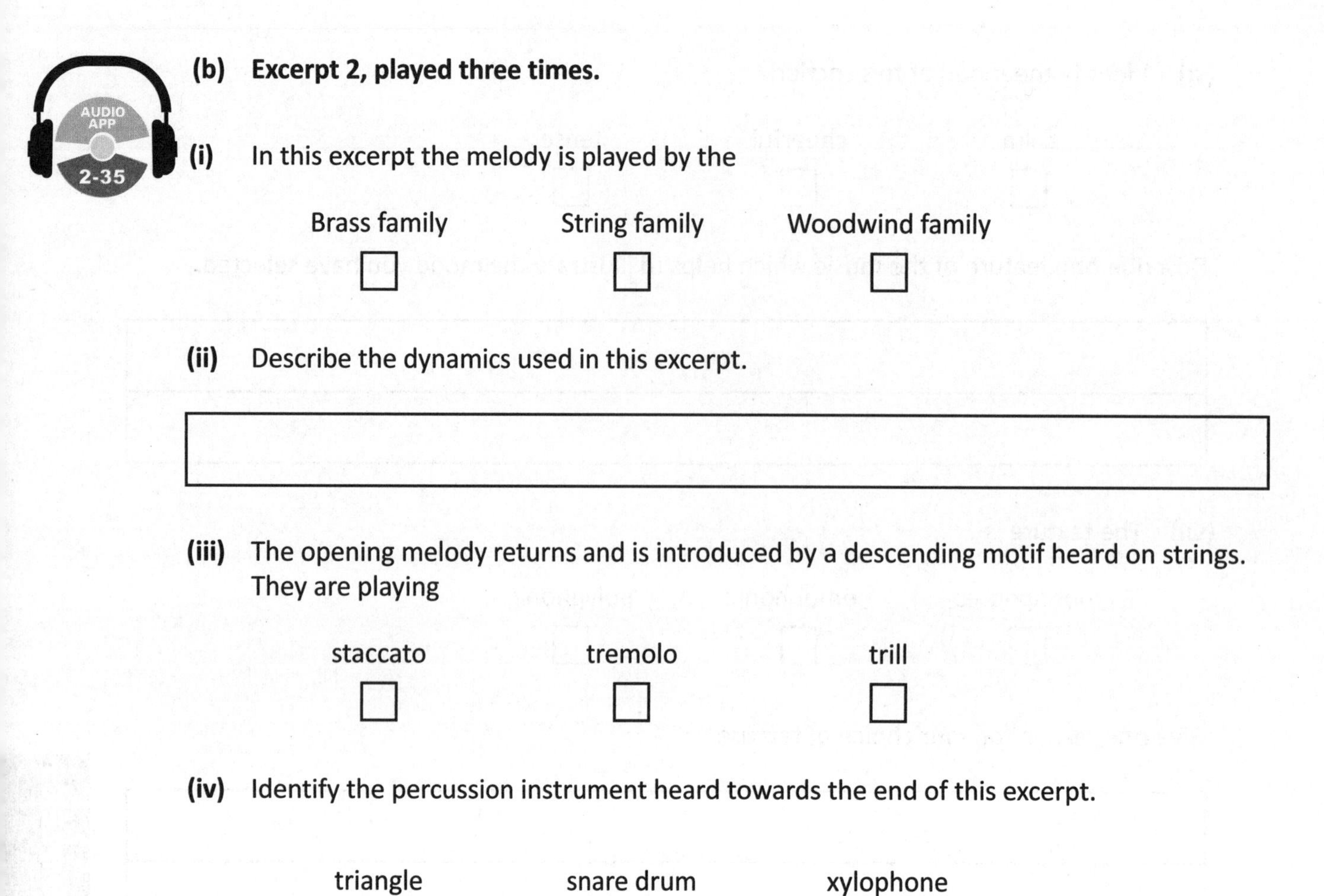

(b) Excerpt 2, played three times.

(i) In this excerpt the melody is played by the

Brass family ☐ String family ☐ Woodwind family ☐

(ii) Describe the dynamics used in this excerpt.

(iii) The opening melody returns and is introduced by a descending motif heard on strings. They are playing

staccato ☐ tremolo ☐ trill ☐

(iv) Identify the percussion instrument heard towards the end of this excerpt.

triangle ☐ snare drum ☐ xylophone ☐

(c) **Excerpt 3, played three times.**

Listen to the music in this excerpt and complete the following sentences. Choose your answers from the word bank provided

Word bank words

Ascending motifs	**Fast**	**Soft**
Strings	**Descending motifs**	**Slow**
Pizzicato	**Woodwind**	**Sustained notes**
Loud		

(i) The dynamics in this excerpt are ______________________.

(ii) The tempo of the music in this excerpt is ______________________.

(iii) The opening melody is played by the ______________________ family.

(iv) The melody features ______________________.

(v) Strings play ______________________ in the accompaniment, in the later section of this excerpt.

(vi) Identify and describe **two** differences between this excerpt and excerpt 2. Refer to both excerpts in your answer.

AUDIO APP 2-35

AUDIO APP 2-36

Excerpt 2 and excerpt 3 will be played **once** only.

i.
ii.

SAMPLE C

(d) Excerpt 2, played once.

(i) Prokofiev composed this music to represent the feud between two families in Shakespeare's play. Comment on **two** features of this piece which help to illustrate this mood for the listener.

i.
ii.

(ii) Name **one** piece of illustrative music that you have studied and briefly describe how the composer depicts characters, nature, emotions or moods in the work you have studied.

Composer:	Piece:

(iii) Suggest **one** instrument suitable for conveying each of the following moods and give **one** reason for each choice.

Mood	**Instrument**	**Reason for choice of instrument**
Triumphant		
Sadness		
Fear		

(iv) An instrument's unique sound is known as

texture ☐ tonality ☐ timbre ☐

(v) Describe the role tonality can play in illustrating moods or emotions in music.

(vi) Describe the role dynamics can play in illustrative music.

SAMPLE C

Roughwork:

Question 5

There is no music heard on the recording for this question.

(a) Define the term **playlist**.

(b) Suggest **one** reason why playlists are popular with young people today.

(c) List **two** scenarios where people will access and listen to a playlist.

i.
ii.

SAMPLE C

(d) Choose **one** local event or community celebration from the list below. Summarise two things you need to consider when building your playlist for your chosen event.

- ☐ Fleadh Cheoil
- ☐ a Christmas fair
- ☐ school sports day
- ☐ St. Patrick's Day celebrations
- ☐ the commemoration of a local historical figure

Write your answer in the box below.

i.
ii.

(e) Describe one genre or style of music that would suit the event or celebration you have chosen.

(f) Indicate **two** songs you would choose for your playlist in the grid below, giving reasons why you are including each song, referring to musical features.

Track	Song title	Reason for including this song
1		
2		

(g) Name an internet platform/website/app where you can share this playlist with others.

Question 6

There is no music heard on the recording for this question.

(a) Explain the term **copyright**.

(b) Identify and explain **one** of the principles of music property rights.

(c) Describe how copyright laws benefit composers and songwriters.

(d) Comment on the impact copyright law has on how music is shared and published.

(e) Name **one** organisation which collects royalties on behalf of composers in Ireland, or promotes the work of Irish composers.

Do not write on this page

Junior Cycle Final Examination
Sample Paper D

Music

Common Level

SAMPLE D

1 hour 30 minutes

280 marks

Examination Number					

Day and Month of Birth					For example, 3rd February is entered as 0302

Instructions

Write your examination number and date of birth in the boxes on the front cover.

There are six questions in this examination paper. Answer all questions.

- Write your answers in blue or black pen. You may use pencil for staff and graphic notation.
- Write your answers in the spaces provided in this booklet.
- Before the examination begins, listen carefully to the test excerpt. If you cannot hear the recording clearly, inform the Superintendent immediately. An Example of this is on CD1 Track 1 and on the Edco Audio App.
- There will be suitable pauses throughout for you to read and answer questions.

Do not write on this page

SAMPLE D

Question 1

(a) One excerpt from *Star Wars IV*, played three times.

Listen to the music in this excerpt and complete the following questions. Choose your answers from the word bank provided.

Word bank words

Brass	Fanfare	Fast
Woodwind	Cymbals	Loud
Pizzicato	Triangle	Soft

Excerpt 1

An excerpt from *Star Wars IV* will be heard.

(i) In the introduction, the main melody is played by ______________________.

(ii) This melody features ______________________ on strings.

(iii) The percussion instrument ______________________ can be heard in this excerpt.

(iv) The tempo of this excerpt is ______________________.

(v) The dynamics in this excerpt are ______________________.

(vi) A new melody is introduced and is played by

woodwind ☐ brass ☐ strings ☐

(b) Excerpt 1, played once only.

This is a piece of illustrative music used in the film *Star Wars: Episode IV – A New Hope* in 1977. The music in this excerpt represents the character Luke Skywalker, the hero of the *Star Wars* movie. Luke is a rebellious, headstrong character who is also kind and caring.

(i) Identify **two** musical features heard in this excerpt and describe how these features illustrate the character of Luke Skywalker.

i.
ii.

(ii) Write about one piece of illustrative music which you have studied and describe how the composer has illustrated characters, emotions, nature or moods in this piece of music.

Name of composer
Title of composition
Description

SAMPLE D

Question 2

(a) Three audio clips played three times. Listen and identify the correct time signature for each excerpt.

Time Signature	$\frac{3}{4}$	$\frac{4}{4}$	$\frac{6}{8}$
Audio Clip 1			
Audio Clip 2			
Audio Clip 3			

(b) (i) Explain the term **body percussion**.

(ii) Design a body percussion pattern for the rhythm pattern below. Write your body percussion directions in the boxes under each rhythm in the pattern below. Use words or symbols to indicate how this pattern should be performed.

Composing Task:

(c) **(i)** Compose your own melody in the key of F major to the given rhythm to complete the tune. End on the keynote/doh.

(ii) Add suitable phrasing

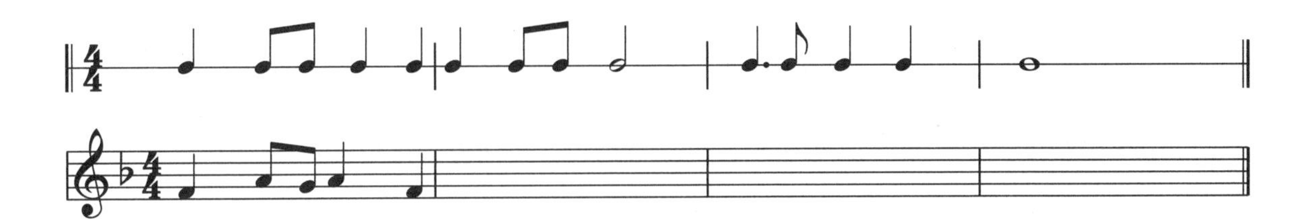

(ii) Suggest **one** instrument suitable to play your composition.

(iii) What advice would you give performers rehearsing to perform this composition?

(iv) What makes a good performance?

Suggest **two** criteria for reviewing a live performance. List the two criteria and describe what you would look out for in a performance in order to meet the criteria in each case.

Criteria	**Description**
i.	
ii.	

Question 3

(a) Excerpt 1, a version of 'Inisheer', played three times.

(i) The accompaniment is played by

(ii) Identify the Irish traditional instrument playing the melody in this excerpt.

Organ	Uilleann pipes	Flute
☐	☐	☐

(iii) The texture of this excerpt is

monophonic	homophonic	polyphonic
☐	☐	☐

(iv) The form of the tune is AABB. This is also known as

unitary	binary	ternary
☐	☐	☐

(v) Identify one melodic feature of the melody in this excerpt.

(vi) Give a reason for your choice of style.

(vi) The style of this performance is

classical	traditional	contemporary
☐	☐	☐

(b) Listen to the excerpt and answer the questions below.

The melody of 'Inisheer' is printed below for you. The excerpt will be played **once** only.

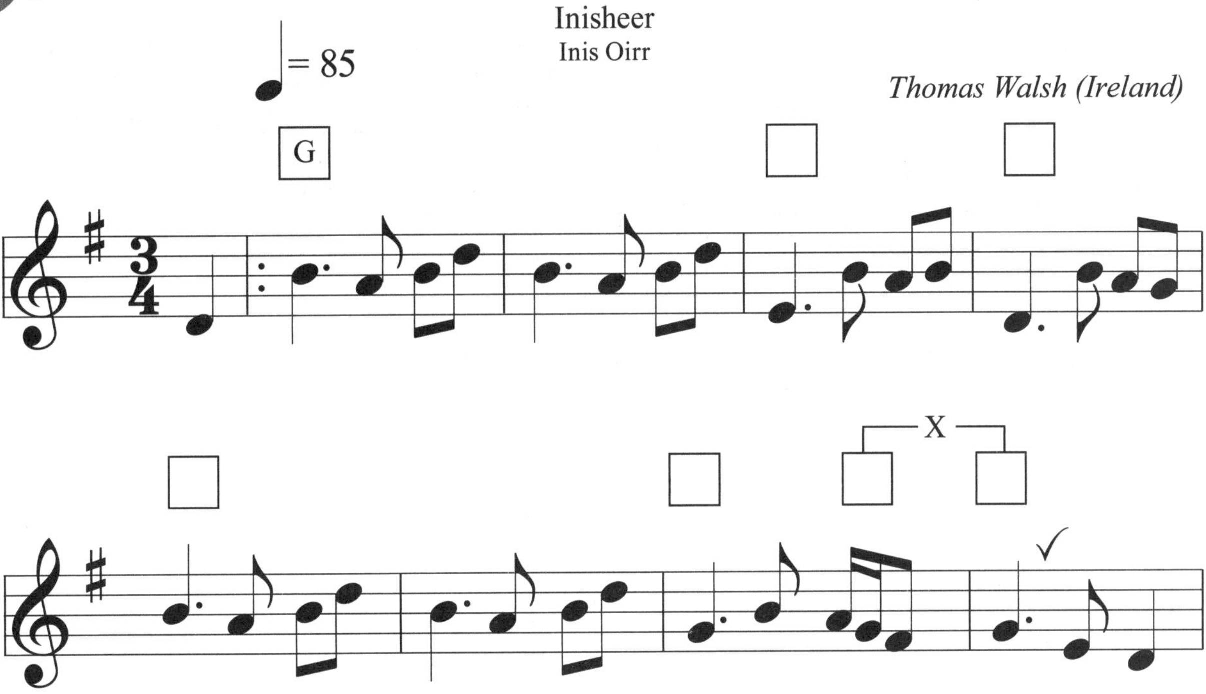

(i) Identify the key signature of this tune.

C minor	D major	G major	G minor
☐	☐	☐	☐

(ii) Composing Task.

Insert suitable chord symbols in the six empty boxes provided to add harmony to the Inisheer melody.

Chord Bank Grid – Key of G major

Notes of Chord	D B G	E C A	F♯ D B	G E C	A F♯ D	B G E	C A F♯
Chord symbol	G	Am	Bm	C	D	Em	F♯°
Roman numeral	I	ii	iii	IV	V	vi	vii°

SAMPLE D

(iii) There is cadence indicated on the score marked X.

(a) Write the chord progression for this cadence in Roman Numerals.

(b) select the cadence that matches this chord progression. A sample is given below to guide you.

	Chord Progression	Perfect Cadence	Plagal Cadence	Imperfect Cadence
Sample	IV – I	☐	✓	☐
X	☐ – ☐	☐	☐	☐

(iv) Suggest a suitable instrument to provide the harmonic support and which is in keeping with the style of this performance.

(v) Write about one traditional folk song that you have studied. Describe two features of this song.

Roughwork

SAMPLE D

AUDIO APP 2-43

Question 4

(a) Excerpt 1, played three times.

(i) Identify the instrument that plays the chord progression in this excerpt.

(ii) The tonality of the excerpt is

major ☐ minor ☐

(iii) The chords are performed as

Broken chords ☐ Block chords ☐

(iv) Reverb has been applied to this recording. Suggest one other processing effect that you would add to this recording.

(v) Describe the impact this processing effect would have on the recording.

(b) (i) The chord progression heard in this excerpt is **C–F–Am–G–C** in C major. Many songs in the popular tradition use a similar chord progression. Name two songs you have studied which feature the same or similar chord progressions.

Song 1	
Song 2	

(ii) What chord progression features in the songs you have named?

Chords:

(iii) The two songs you have named above feature similar chord progressions. Describe two differences between the music heard in the two songs that you have chosen.

Difference 1:
Difference 2:

SAMPLE D

Question 5

Four excerpts, played three times.

This question is based on a performance of the Irish song 'She Moved Through the Fair'.

Excerpt 1

Listen to a performance of the first verse of the song 'She Moved Through The Fair'. There are four phrases in this verse.

(a) **(i)** The melody is sung by a f_______ vocalist.

(ii) The texture is ___________.

(iii) The accompaniment plays a d______.

(iv) The performance is in f____ rhythm.

(v) Describe one traditional feature of the singer's performance.

(b) Listen to this excerpt from verse two of 'She Moved Through the Fair' and answer the questions below.

AUDIO APP 2-45

Excerpt 2, played three times.

The lyrics for the second verse from this song are printed below.

Line 1 ● *She went away from me and moved through the fair*

Line 2 *And fondly I watched her move here and move there*

Line 3 *And then she went onwards, just one star awake*

Line 4 *Like the swans in the evening move over the lake*

(i) Line 1 has a red circle beside it. Draw a circle beside another line that has the same melody.

(ii) Draw a different shape beside the remaining line(s) to illustrate the structure of the verse.

(iii) These shapes represent the form

- AABB ☐
- ABBA ☐
- ABAB ☐

(iv) The tonality of this performance is

- major ☐
- minor ☐

(v) The melody line features

- ornamentation ☐
- syncopation ☐
- a repeated final note ☐

(vi) Circle **one** word from line three and **one** word from line four where you can hear a chord change in the accompaniment.

3 *And then she went onwards, just one star awake*

4 *Like the swans in the evening move over the lake*

SAMPLE D

(c) Two excerpts, played three times.

Excerpt 1, played three times.

AUDIO APP 2-46

(i) The first phrase will be played on the piano. There will be a pause after each playing. Use the rhythm provided to help you to insert the **five** missing melody notes in bars 2 and 3.

Excerpt 2, played three times.

AUDIO APP 2-47

(ii) The melody for the second phrase is printed below. Insert suitable chords in the boxes provided. A chord bank has been provided for you.

Chord Bank – D major

Notes of chord	A F♯ D	B G E	C♯ A F♯	D B G	E C♯ A	F♯ D B	G E C♯
Chord symbol	D	Em	F♯m	G	A	Bm	C♯°
Roman numeral	I	ii	iii	IV	V	vi	vii°

(iii) Write the chord progression that the final chords create in roman numerals. Select the cadence that matches this chord progression in the grid below.

	Chord Progression	**Perfect Cadence**	**Plagal Cadence**	**Imperfect Cadence**
Cadence	☐–☐	☐	☐	☐

(d) **(i)** The composer of 'She Moved Through the Fair' is unknown. The song was collected by Hubert Hughes in Donegal. Before this, the song's survival had relied on the **oral tradition**. Explain this term.

(ii) Name **one** piece of traditional music you have studied.

(iii) Name **one** traditional composer or performer you have researched.

(iv) List **two** features of traditional Irish music.

i.
ii.

(v) Many versions of folk songs like 'She Moved Through the Fair' exist. Suggest **one** reason why this is the case.

SAMPLE D

(vi) Choose **one** piece of traditional Irish or folk music that you have studied and compared. Name the performers of each arrangement and identify **one similarity** and **one difference** between the two arrangements of the piece that you have chosen.

Name of piece:

	Arrangement 1	Arrangement 2
Performer/s		
Similarity		
Difference		

Question 6

(a) **(i)** Explain the term **found sound**.

(ii) Look at the image below and answer the questions that follow.

Suggest **two** features of this image that you could illustrate through sound. Describe the two sounds that you would use to illustrate them, giving reasons for your choice.

Feature from image	**Description**
i.	i.
ii.	ii.

SAMPLE D

(iii) Create a symbolic representation for each of the found sounds referred to in question (ii).

Sound 1:	Sound 2:

(iv) Explain the purpose of graphic scores.

(v) Identify **one** piece of information which might be shared by the composer of a graphic score so that others can perform the work.

Do not write on this page

SAMPLE D

Roughwork

Junior Cycle Final Examination
Sample Paper E

Music

Common Level

1 hour 30 minutes

280 marks

Examination Number

Day and Month of Birth

For example, 3rd February is entered as 0302

SAMPLE E

Instructions

Write your examination number and date of birth in the boxes on the front cover.

There are six questions in this examination paper. Answer all questions.

- Write your answers in blue or black pen. You may use pencil for staff and graphic notation.
- Write your answers in the spaces provided in this booklet.
- Before the examination begins, listen carefully to the test excerpt. If you cannot hear the recording clearly, inform the Superintendent immediately. An Example of this is on CD1 Track 1 and on the Edco Audio App.
- There will be suitable pauses throughout for you to read and answer questions.

Do not write on this page

SAMPLE E

Question 1

Two excerpts, played three times.

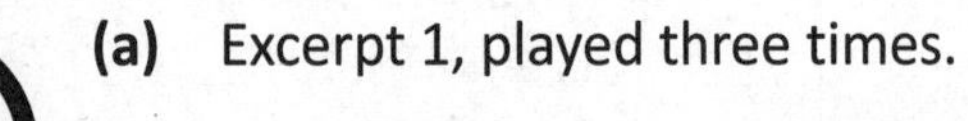

(a) Excerpt 1, played three times.

An excerpt from the Irish ballad 'Grace' played three times.

The lyrics of the verse are shown below. The shape of the melody for lines 1 and 2 is represented by graphics

Line 1
As we gather in the chapel here in old Kilmainham gaol

Line 2
I think about these past few weeks, oh will they say we've failed

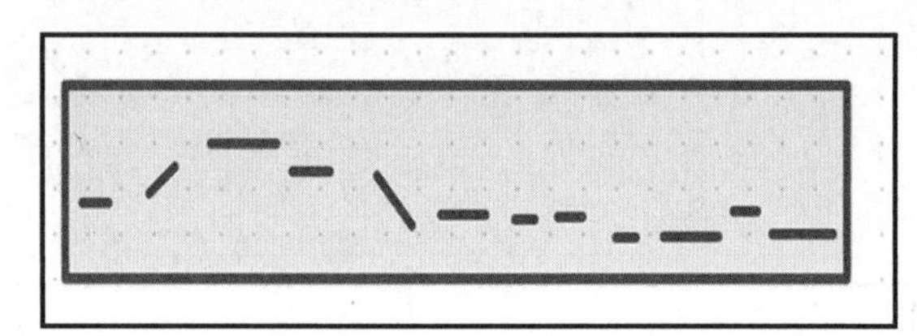

Line 3
From our school days, they have told us we must yearn for liberty

Line 4
Yet all I want, in this dark place, is to have you here with me

(i) select the graphic which best represents the melody in **line 3**

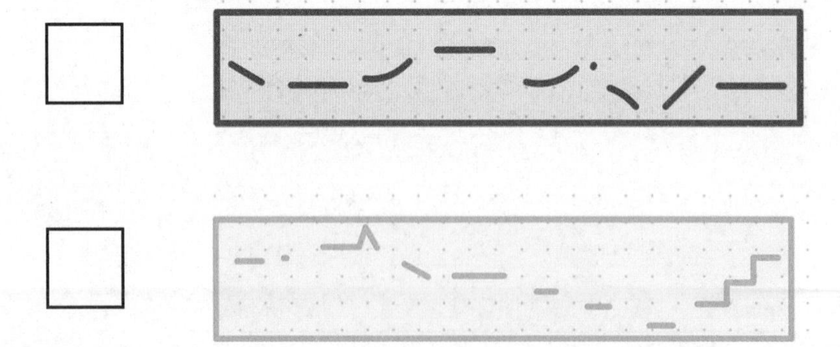

(ii) The form of this song is

ABAB	ABBA	ABAC
☐	☐	☐

(iii) This form is known as

unitary	binary	ternary
☐	☐	☐

(iv) Using shapes create a visual representation of this form

(v) Idenitfy the number of bars introduction which are heard before the singer enters

4	6	8
☐	☐	☐

(vi) Identify the type of song heard in this excerpt

love song	working song	drinking song
☐	☐	☐

(b) Excerpt 2, played three times.

The lyrics of verse two are printed below. The boxes around the lyrics in lines 1 and 2 show where the chords change

(i) insert boxes around two other words where you hear a chord change.

1 Now, I **[know]** it's hard for you my love, to **[ever]** un **[derstand]**

2 The **[love]** I bear for **[these]** brave men, my **[love]** for this dear **[land]**

3 But when Pádhraic called me to his side, down in the GPO

4 I had to leave my own sick bed, to him I had to go.

(ii) Describe **one** difference between excerpt 1 and excerpt 2.

(iii) Describe **one** similarity between excerpt 1 and excerpt 2.

This song was written in 1985 by Frank and Seán O'Meara and it has been recorded by many musicians including The Dubliners and Rod Stewart.

(iv) Name **one** composition or song you have studied by an Irish composer or songwriter.

Name of song/composition
Name of songwriter/composer

Composers and songwriters make their livelihood from their music.

(v) Describe one way in which the music of Irish performers is promoted on local or national Irish media.

(vi) Explain one way in which Irish musicians benefit from royalties.

(vii) Name one organisation responsible for collecting royalties on behalf of Irish songwriters and performers.

SAMPLE E

Roughwork

Question 2

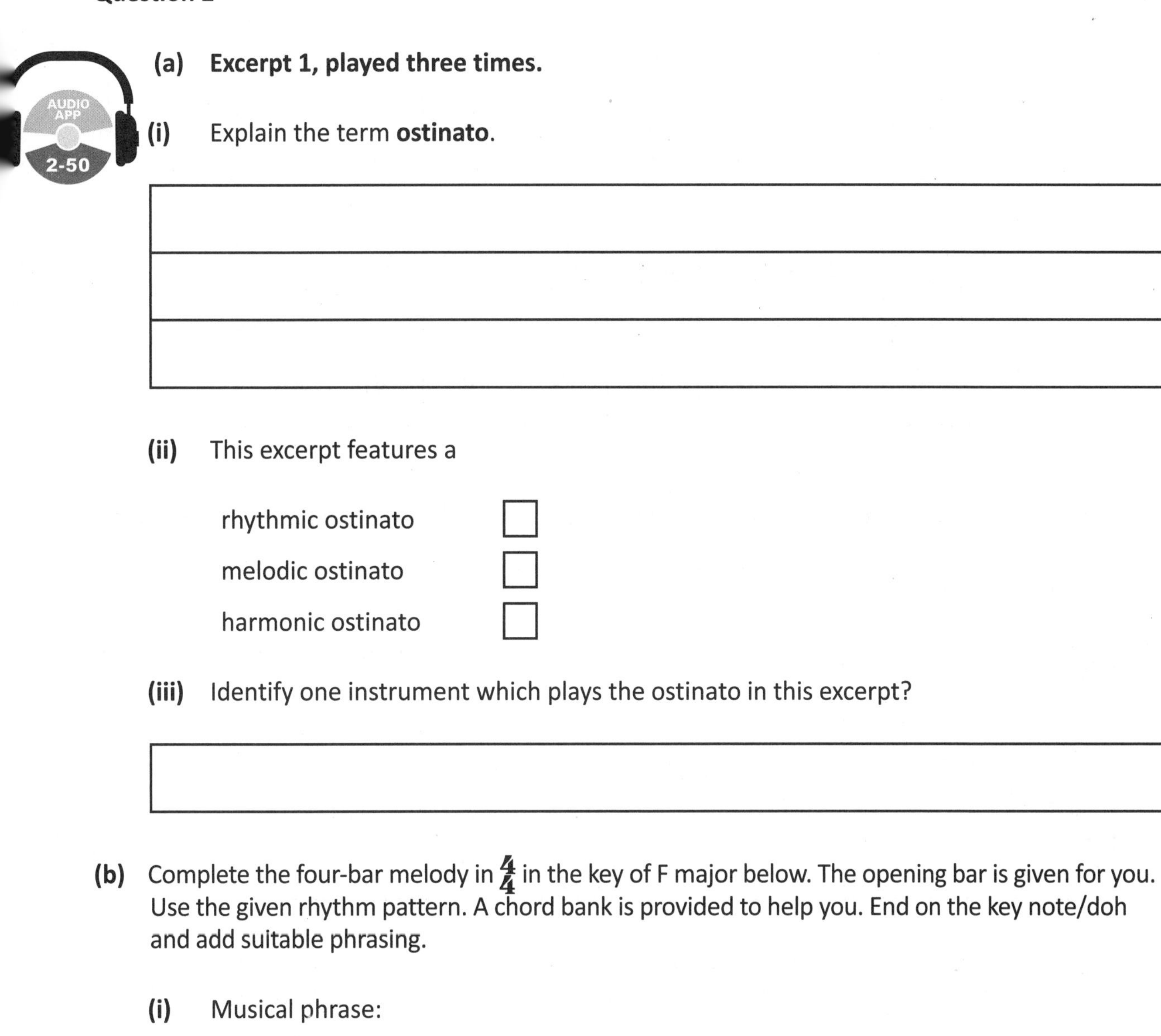

(a) Excerpt 1, played three times.

(i) Explain the term **ostinato**.

(ii) This excerpt features a

rhythmic ostinato ☐

melodic ostinato ☐

harmonic ostinato ☐

(iii) Identify one instrument which plays the ostinato in this excerpt?

(b) Complete the four-bar melody in $\frac{4}{4}$ in the key of F major below. The opening bar is given for you. Use the given rhythm pattern. A chord bank is provided to help you. End on the key note/doh and add suitable phrasing.

(i) Musical phrase:

(ii) Support this phrase by creating a one-bar rhythmic ostinato to accompany it.

Rhythmic ostinato: $\frac{4}{4}$

SAMPLE E

Chord Bank – F major

Notes of chord	C A F	D B♭ G	E C A	F D B♭	G E C	A F D	B♭ G E
Chord symbol	F	Gm	Am	B♭	C	Dm	Em°
Roman numeral	I	ii	iii	IV	V	vi	vii°

(iii) Select **instruments** to perform this composition and explain why you have chosen them.

Melody instrument:	
Reason for choice	
Rhythm instrument:	
Reason for choice	

(iv) Suggest **one** processing effect you would add to a recording of your completed composition and describe the impact this effect would have on the recording.

(c) (i) Compose a melodic phrase in B♭ major using the opening bar given below. Make sure to keynote/doh. Add suitable phrasing.

Write your phrase on the stave provided.

Rhythm

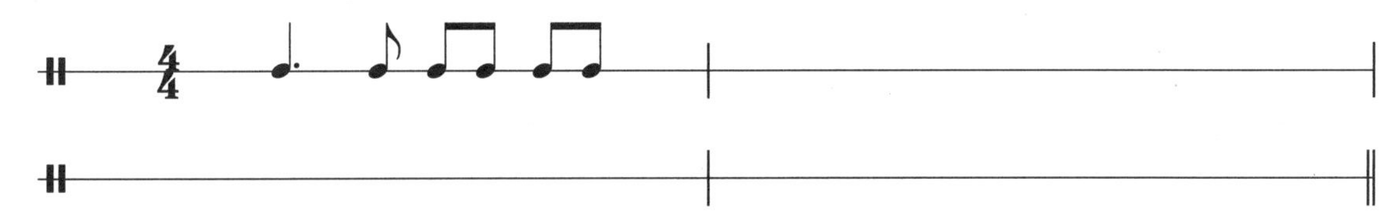

Melody

Moderate speed *(Moderato)*

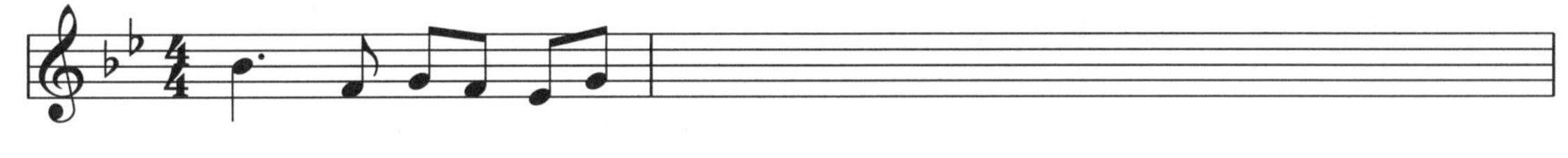

(ii) Suggest a suitable woodwind instrument to play this melody.

(iii) Explain the term **improvisation**.

(iv) Compose a four-chord harmonic progression in B♭ major which could be recorded and improvised over by a performer.

Insert your chord progression below, using chord names. Do not use roman numerals here.

Chord 1	Chord 2	Chord 3	Chord 4

Notes of chord	F D B♭	G E♭ C	A F D	B♭ G E♭	C A F	D B♭ G	E♭ C A
Chord symbol	B♭	Cm	Dm	E♭	F	Gm	A°
Roman numeral	I	ii	iii	IV	V	vi	vii°

SAMPLE E

Question 3

One excerpt, played three times.

(a) (i) Design a suitable harmonic accompaniment for this melody. Insert suitable chord symbols in the six empty boxes provided to add harmony to this melody. The first chord is completed for you.

Insert your harmonic accompaniment on the stave provided below.

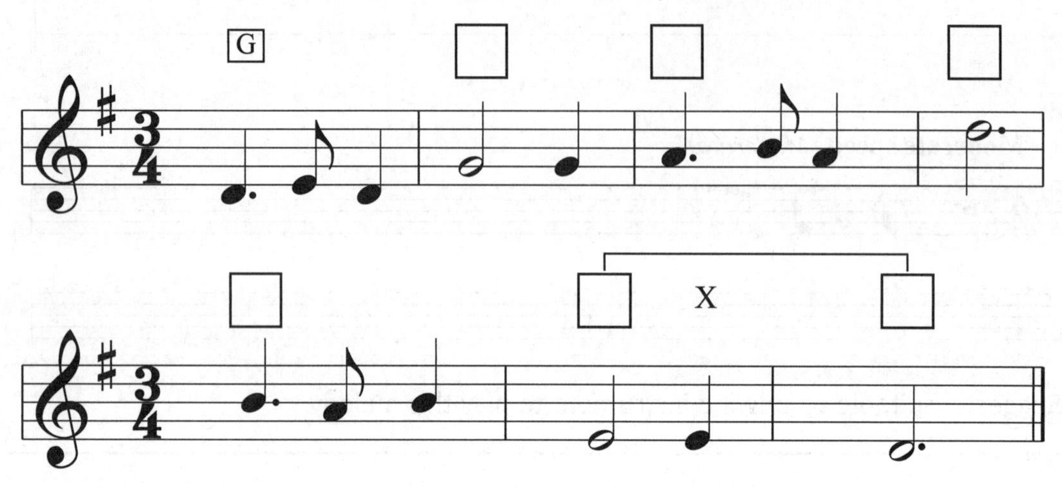

Rough work

Notes of chord	D B G	E C A	F♯ D B	G E C	A F♯ D	B G E	C A F♯
Chord symbol	G	Am	Bm	C	D	Em	F♯°
Roman numeral	I	ii	iii	IV	V	vi	vii°

(ii) Write the chord progression that the final chords create in roman numerals. Select the cadence that matches this chord progression in the grid below.

	Chord Progression	Perfect Cadence	Plagal Cadence	Imperfect Cadence
Cadence	☐-☐	☐	☐	☐

One excerpt, played three times.

(b) The chord progression **I–IV–V–I** will be played for you on the piano.

(i) Design a rhythmic accompaniment for use with this harmonic progression.

Write your rhythmic accompaniment on the rhythm line.

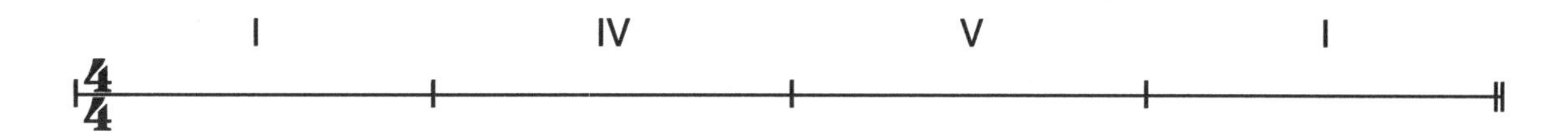

Do your rough work in the box provided.

(ii) Suggest **two** instruments suitable to perform this piece together.

Harmonic progression/chords:
Rhythmic accompaniment:

SAMPLE E

(iii) Suggest a suitable instrument to improvise over this harmonic and rhythmic motif.

(iv) Give **one** reason for your choice.

(v) Name **one** genre or style of music which features improvisation.

(c) One excerpt, played once only

(i) Composing Task

Insert suitable chords in the 10 empty boxes provided to add harmony to Kumbaya

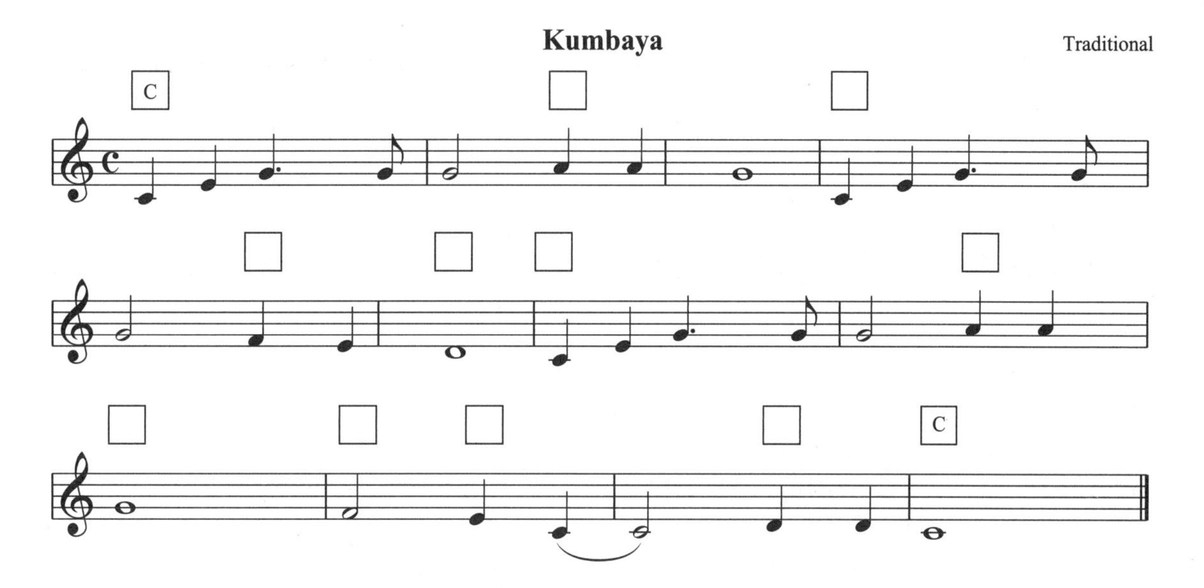

Chord Bank – C major

Notes of Chord	G E C	A F D	B G E	C A F	D B G	E C A	F D B
Chord symbol	C	Dm	Em	F	G	Am	B°
Roman numeral	I	ii	iii	IV	V	vi	vii°

(ii) Identify the cadence created by the final two chords in 'Kumbaya'.

SAMPLE E

Question 4

(a) An excerpt, played four times.

(i) A four-bar phrase will be played four times.

Identify the rhythm pattern in bar 2 and add the **six** missing melody notes to bars 3 and 4.

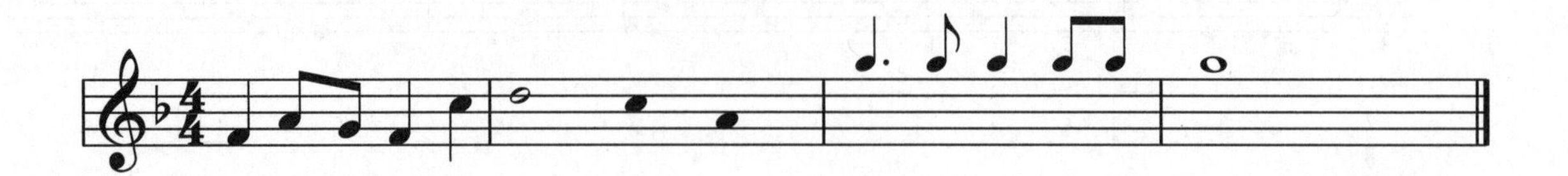

(b) Three excerpts, played twice

Excerpt 1

Excerpt 2

Excerpt 3

(i) Three excerpts will be played for you.

Each excerpt begins on the **tonic chord I**. Indicate which excerpt uses the harmonic progression **I–V–I**.

Excerpt 1 ☐ Excerpt 2 ☐ Excerpt 3 ☐

(ii) Chords added to a melodic line provide which of the following?

Melodic support ☐ Rhythmic support ☐ Harmonic support ☐

(iii) List **two** songs which you have studied that are based on the same chord progression.

i.
ii.

Roughwork:

SAMPLE E

Question 5

Three excerpts, played three times.

This excerpt is the opening section of 'Erlkönig', an art song by Franz Schubert. Schubert took the words from one of Goethe's poem and set them to music. The poem depicts a father racing through the forest on his horse with his sick son. His son claims to see a supernatural being called the Erl-King.

Excerpt 1, played three times.

(a) Listen to the music in this excerpt and answer the questions.

The music for the opening bars is provided for you.

(i) Identify the instrument which plays the introduction.

(ii) Identify one feature of the introduction.

(iii) The vocalist is

male ☐

female ☐

The vocal range of the vocalist is

soprano	☐	tenor	☐
alto	☐	bass	☐

(iv) Identify the meaning of the following symbols marked X, Y and Z on the Erlkonig sheet music.

(a) This rhythmic feature is known as:

- ☐ A trill
- ☐ A triplet
- ☐ A tremolo

(b) This symbol indicates:

- ☐ A fermata
- ☐ A crotchet rest
- ☐ A quaver

(c) *f* This symbol tells the musicians to:

- ☐ Slow down
- ☐ Play loudly
- ☐ Gradually get quieter

(v) Explain the term **ostinato**.

(vi) Describe the use of ostinato in the accompaniment.

SAMPLE E

(vii) Schubert creates a tense and frightened mood in this piece. He is trying to illustrate a father's fear and panic as he seeks help for his sick child. Choose **two** elements from the list below and describe how these elements help to create this mood.

Circle the two elements you have chosen to write about.

Dynamics **Tempo** **Texture** **Instruments** **Rhythm**

i.
ii.

AUDIO APP
2-59

(b) Excerpt 2, played three times.

This excerpt is the first verse of 'Wiegenlied', a lullaby also composed by Franz Schubert. The opening melody is printed for you below.

Schla - fe, Schla - fe, hol - der, sü - ßer_ Kna - be,

(i) The vocalist is a

	Soprano	Alto	Tenor	Bass
Voices	☐	☐	☐	☐

(ii) Suggest a tempo marking for this excerpt.

(iii) The texture of this performance is

monophonic ☐ homophonic ☐ polyphonic ☐

(iv) Identify one feature of the singer's performance.

(v) The accompaniment features

Ascending scales ☐ Descending scales ☐ Broken chords ☐

SAMPLE E

(c) Excerpt 3, played four times.

This excerpt is a performance of Brahms's 'Lullaby'. This lullaby was composed by Brahms for his friend after the birth of her son. As in Schubert's 'Erlkönig', the lyrics for this song are taken from a German folk poem. The music for verse 1 is printed for you below.

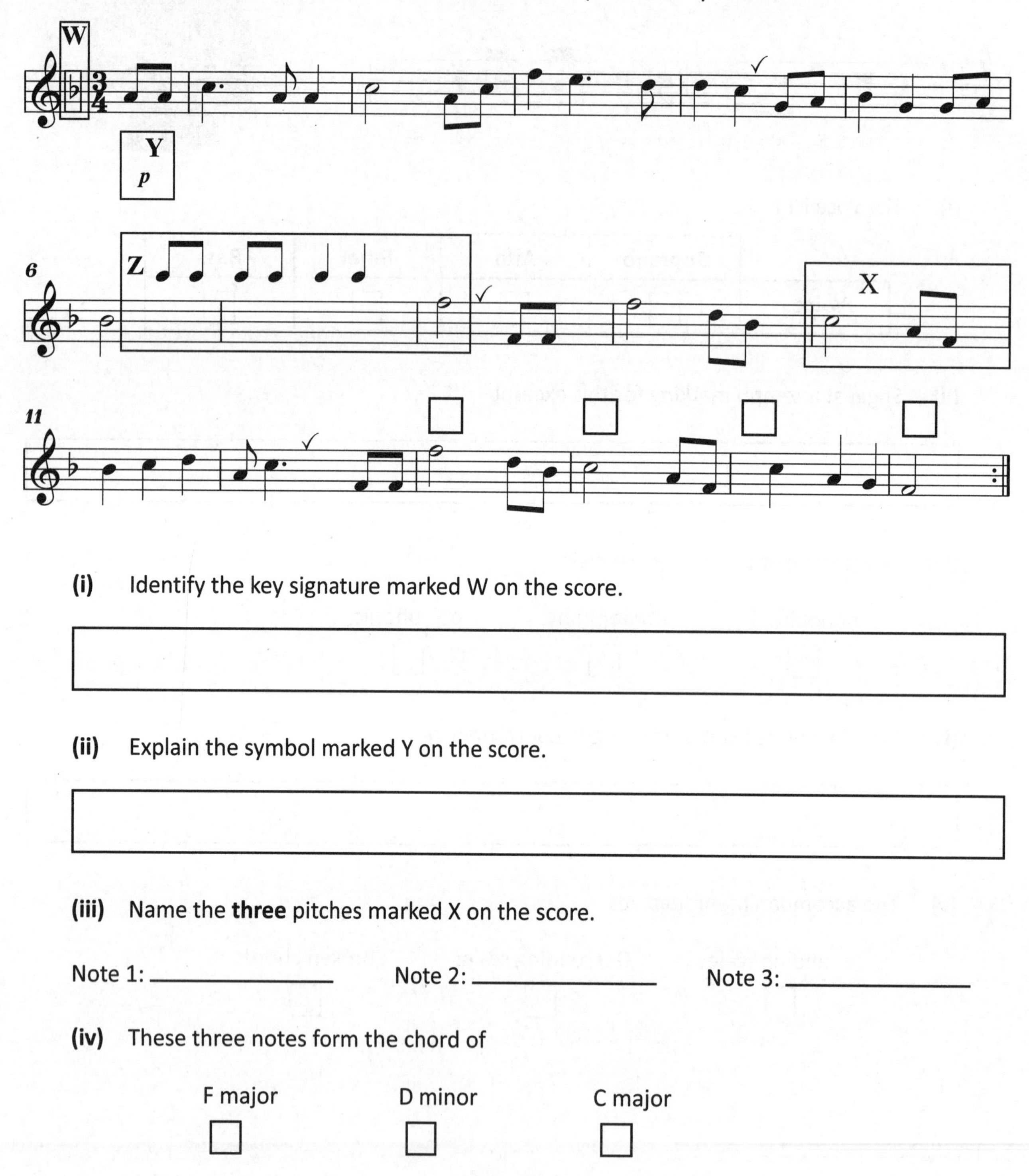

(i) Identify the key signature marked W on the score.

(ii) Explain the symbol marked Y on the score.

(iii) Name the **three** pitches marked X on the score.

Note 1: __________ Note 2: __________ Note 3: __________

(iv) These three notes form the chord of

F major ☐ D minor ☐ C major ☐

(v) Insert the missing pitches marked at Z. The rhythm is shown above the stave to help you. Write your answer on the stave.

(vi) Circle an octave leap in the melody line. Mark your answer on the stave.

(vii) Indicate suitable chords to provide harmony for the last line of the music. Write the chord names in the boxes printed above the stave. Do not use roman numerals

Chord Bank – F major

Notes of chord	C A F	D B♭ G	E C A	F D B♭	G E C	A F D	B♭ G E
Chord symbol	F	Gm	Am	B♭	C	Dm	Em°
Roman numeral	I	ii	iii	IV	V	vi	vii°

Question 6

(a) There is no music on the recording for this question.

'Erlkönig' from question 5a and Brahms's 'Lullaby' from question 5c are examples of **art songs**. Art songs are poems which have been set to music for vocals with simple accompaniment.

- Schubert and Brahms are both composers from the **Romantic era**.
- These works are examples of **art songs**; the lyrics in both songs are taken from German poems.
- Franz Schubert was born in **Austria** and Johann Brahms was born in **Germany**.

(i) Name a music era or style of music that you have studied.

(ii) Share information about two pieces of music that you have compared, composed by **two different** composers from **two different** countries.

	Composer	Musical Example	Country of Origin
i.			
ii.			

(iii) Write about **two** features of the style or era you have studied.

i.
ii.

(iv) Identify **one** aural signpost in each one of the pieces that you have named and explain why you have chosen it.

Name of piece	Aural signpost	Reason for choice

(b) There is no music on the recording for this question.

(i) Explain the term **property rights**.

(ii) List two ways in which copyright laws protect artists in Ireland.

i.
ii.

(iii) In what ways could the Irish music industry be damaged by those who break copyright law?

(iv) Describe one example of copyright law infringement.

(c) **(i)** Name **one** composer or songwriter of traditional music that you have studied.

(ii) Name **one** piece of music composed by the composer or songwriter you have named.

(iii) Name **one** local or national radio broadcaster.

(iv) What role can local and national broadcasting and media organisations play in promoting the success of Irish music and performers nationally and globally? Why is it important that they support the work of these artists?

Practical Preparation and Programme Note

Assessment of Junior Cycle Music has four components

Component	What?	When?	Marks and Percentage
Classroom-Based Assessment 1	Compositional Portfolio	2nd Year	Descriptor on JCPA
Classroom-Based Assessment 2	Programme Note relating to Practical exam	3rd Year – Completed in advance of Practical exams	Descriptor on JCPA
Practical Exam	Perform 3 pieces with an unprepared test	3rd Year – March/April	30% 120 Marks
Written Exam		3rd Year – June	70% 280 Marks

There are two Classroom-Based Assessments (CBAs) for Music at Junior Cycle. CBA1 is completed in 2nd year. In 3rd year you will complete CBA2 in the weeks leading up to your Practical Exam, which usually takes place during March or April. Descriptors for your CBAs will be printed on your Junior Cycle Profile of Achievement (JCPA) as a record of your learning over the three years of Junior Cycle. CBA2 is linked in with your Practical Exam. You are required to perform three pieces of music and complete one unprepared test on the day of your Practical Exam.

The material in this additional chapter has been added to your exam papers to provide you with space to plan and prepare for your Practical Exam and for the completion of your Programme Note.

Supports have also been designed to help you to prepare for the Unprepared Tests which are worth 20% of the practical grade. Audio tracks for Aural Memory tests and Sight-Reading samples are also included. Engagement with these will help you to prepare for this part of your exam.

Classroom-Based Assessment 2: The Programme Note

For this Classroom-Based Assessment you will prepare a programme note to inform an audience about the content of your upcoming performance, which itself will comprise the Practical Examination.

Preparing for CBA2

You may find it easier to gather information for use in your Programme Note as you learn your pieces. Finding out about the pieces you are learning will help you to progress with your performance. Researching the composers' intentions and discovering important aural signposts will help you to perform these pieces with a greater appreciation of how they should be performed.

Preparing a Song for Performance

Take time to explore the basic facts and features of the pieces you want to perform.

- Time signature
- Tonality/key signature and range
- Tempo
- The name of the composer and the lyricist

Whenever we attend a live performance, it is helpful to know some information or background about the performance. What information is usually shared with audience members? How do composers and performers choose to share this information with us? Every piece of music has a unique combination of elements which can be appreciated. Sharing information about the composer, the inspiration for their work, the story or mood of the music, the instruments chosen and things we should listen out for can all be identified and explained to us in a programme note.

Choose one of the songs you have performed this year and write a short programme note for it. Good research skills will be required! Include background information, features of the music and one musical point of interest we should listen out for.

	Composer	Genre
Song Title		
Points of interest	(i)	(ii)
Melodic Snapshots		

Practical Pieces – Logging Your Learning

Use the grid below to help you track important information about the pieces you learn as the year progresses. This will be helpful to return to once you have chosen the three pieces you will commit to performing on the day of the exam.

Name of Piece:	Composer:	Genre/Historical Era/Description	Description/Aural Signposts
SAMPLE Sally Gardens (recorder)	Hubert Hughes – Words by W. B. Yeats	Art Song – Love Song 1909 Poem written by W. B. Yeats to reconstruct an old song he had heard called *The Rambling Boys of Pleasure*, published in 1889. The words were set to the music of *The Moorlough Shore* in 1909 by Hubert Hughes	Key of D major Upbeat Love song Traditional Form AABA Octave leap Repeated final note
1.			
2.			
3.			

4.			
5.			
6.			
7.			
8.			
9.			
10.			

CBA2 Preparing Your Programme Note

Your Programme Note should provide information about the pieces you are preparing for your practical exam. A programme note should **inform an audience** about the music they will hear during a performance.

The Assessment Guidelines (October 2019) provide helpful advice, stating that: *'some background information on the lives of the composers or songwriters can provide important insights into their* ***intentions****, and an understanding of the wider context of the music to be performed. Providing the listener and the audience with* ***signposts*** *and indicators of what to listen out for and giving them some interesting anecdotes about the composer/songwriter of the piece, enlightens and enhances the listener's experience.'*

Quick-Think!

What is meant by a composer's intentions?	
What is an aural signpost?	

Programme Note Guidance

Your Programme Note will need to be completed **two weeks in advance of the practical examination**, which usually takes place during March or April each year. Your Programme Note should take no **more than three weeks to complete**, and should be completed with some help and support from your teacher.

There is no set format or layout which must be followed. You must **mention each of the three pieces** you will perform in. Your Programme Note can be as varied and as unique as your performance. You should introduce your performance, the pieces you will perform and whether or not you will perform as a soloist or part of a group. **If you perform as part of a group you must still submit an individual programme note** which explains your role in the performance. If you are the composer of any of the pieces that you will perform, you **should** write about this when writing under the headings suggested below.

The following guidelines have been shared to help you complete your Programme Note.

Programme Notes can include the following:

- A brief introduction to the composers/songwriters (if applicable).
- A description about the historical context of the pieces and the circumstances surrounding the composition.
- One interesting musical point in each piece for the listener/audience to listen out for.
- Famous exponents of a tune or an instrument.
- A description of your role in a group performance.

The following questions should be considered:

- Is this piece typical of the time it was written or collected in?
- What is the most interesting moment in this piece for me?
- What do I want the attention of the listener to be guided towards?
- What is or where is my favourite section of this piece?

Your Programme Note must be submitted to your teacher two weeks before the Practical Exams begin. It is important to remember **that you can present your work in written, digital, visual or audio form, or any other format that is deemed suitable** and is appropriate for capturing the essence of what you would like to communicate to your audience about your performance. It is advised that you spend no more than three weeks researching and completing your Programme Note.

Features of Quality

The Features of Quality are used to decide the level of achievement to be awarded for Classroom-Based Assessments. There are four descriptors:

- Yet to Meet Expectations,
- In Line with Expectations,
- Above Expectations, and
- Exceptional.

Exploring the features of quality helps us to understand how our work will be judged and what the success criteria are for our Programme Notes. These are listed for you below.

Features of Quality: Music: Programme Note
Exceptional • Programme Note offers, to a very high standard, concise, compelling and highly interesting details of the pieces that provide very detailed insights with comprehensive supports for the listener • In-depth and very detailed information is provided on the historical context or purpose of composition • The biographical details of the composer/songwriter/exponents of the style show evidence of a very high level of initiative in research.
Above expectations • Programme Note offers concise, compelling and interesting details of the pieces that are very clear and provide detailed insights with very good supports for the listener • In-depth and detailed information is provided on the historical context or purpose of composition • The biographical details of the composer/songwriter/exponents of the style show evidence of a high level of initiative in research.
In line with expectations • Programme Note adequately offers a few interesting facts and details of the pieces that are clear and provide some insights with good supports for the listener • Adequate information and background is provided on the historical context or purpose of composition • The biographical details of the composer/songwriter/exponents of the style show evidence of some level of initiative in research.
Yet to meet expectations • Programme Note offers limited facts and details of the pieces and provides the listener with little or no insights to support them • Limited information and background is provided on the historical context or purpose of composition • The biographical details of the composer/songwriter/exponents of the style show a lack of evidence of research or independent reading.

Choosing a Programme for Performance

This can be the tricky part! Reflecting on the pieces you have learned will help you to decide which three pieces you would like to prepare for performance in your exam.

What are your top five?

Piece 1	
Piece 2	
Piece 3	
Piece 4	
Piece 5	

Considering the following questions might help you to choose your pieces.

Why I chose this piece, what do I like about it?
How confident do I feel performing this piece?
What performance skills can I show in this piece?
What challenges do I face when I perform this piece?
What areas, if any, need more practice?

Practice Log

Preparing for any performance takes time and commitment. The more you play your pieces, the more familiar they become. Practice with purpose is important too! What part of your performance needs work? Choosing a focus for practice helps you to overcome any challenging parts of your pieces. Starting from this focus point every time you practise ensures that you get the most out of your practice. Once you master one challenge, you can move to the next. Use the chart below to track your progress with practice.

Date:		Piece 1	Piece 2	Piece 3
	Progress:			
	Focus:			
	Progress:			
	Focus:			
	Progress:			
	Focus:			
	Progress:			
	Focus:			
	Progress:			
	Focus:			
	Progress:			
	Focus:			
	Progress:			
	Focus:			

Feedback on My Performances

Teacher feedback will help you to progress! Keep a note of this too!

Date	Piece	Feedback

Creating Your Programme Note

Once you decide on the three pieces you will perform you can begin to plan your Programme Note. It can be in any format you choose. Discuss this with your teacher and consider what format works best for you. You can use the sample Programme Note template below as a structure to follow as you get started. It will help you to research and gather the information you need to include in your Programme Note. It has been designed to help you to organise the information you need for each piece of music that will feature in your Programme Note. **All three pieces must be referred to in the Programme Note that you submit for assessment.**

Sample Programme Note Template

Make copies of this template to create a Programme Note for each of your performances.

Name of Piece:		**Composer/Songwriter**
Genre/Style:	**Medium (voice/instrument):**	
Solo or Group Performance?		

Introduction: Write a short note about the composer/songwriter of your piece.
Context: Describe what was happening in the composer/songwriter's country at the time it was composed.
Circumstances: Why was this piece composed? Does it have a function or purpose? Has this music influenced other compositions?

Aural Signposts:

Identify your favourite part of the piece and one other aural signpost that your audience should listen out for during your performance. Explain why you have chosen to highlight these.

Reflection:

Write a short note on your experiences learning this piece and the role you have in the performance. What challenges did you face, how did you overcome them and why do you enjoy performing this piece?

Other points of interest

Melodic motifs or other features you would like to include can be transcribed onto the staves below.

Practical Exam

The Practical Examination will be allocated 30% of the marks available and will be marked by the State Examinations Commission (SEC).

The Practical Examination will take place during March or April in 3rd year. You will perform three musical songs/ pieces.

- Solo and group performing may be freely mixed.
- Your songs/pieces may also be presented on a variety of instruments or through a combination of voice and instruments.
- Technical control, fluency and musicality will be assessed.
- The standard required will reflect what can be attained in three years of class-based tuition.

On the day of your exam you will also take **one** unprepared test. You will have an opportunity to choose from:

- Aural memory rhythm
- Aural memory melody
- Sight-reading (instrumental/vocal/rhythmic) or
- Improvisation.

Note: Aural memory and sight-reading tests will be four bars long. In the case of improvisation, students will be required to improvise for at least four bars.

Unprepared Tests

A number of unprepared tests have been designed for you below. Aural memory rhythm and aural memory melody tests are available on your audio app. Sight-reading sample unprepared tests are printed for you below.

Do not underestimate the importance of preparing for your unprepared tests. Practise these tests often.

Aural Memory Tests

Each aural memory test will be played three times. You will attempt the test after the second and third playing. Marks will be awarded for your best attempt. SEC Sample aural tests are available from www.examinations.ie

Tracks 2-61 to 2-65 on your Junior Cycle Music Edco Aural App and Teacher's CDs are Sample Aural Memory Rhythm Tests.

Tracks 2-66 to 2-70 on your Junior Cycle Music Edco Aural App and Teacher's CDs are Sample Aural Memory Melody Tests.

Sight Reading Tests

You can take a few moments to read over the sight reading given to you by the examiner on the day of your exam. Take time to review the rhythm and melody closely, paying attention to elements such as key signatures, tempo markings and dynamics where relevant. You have one attempt only at performing this test.

Sight Clapping Practice Tracks

Sight clapping is a new and welcome option in Junior Cycle Music. The samples we have provided here are designed to help you to get started with sight clapping. In your exam you will be required to clap the rhythm tests which are also suited to percussion instruments. You can tap or clap the rhythm pattern in the exam. The audio tracks provided for sample tests (I) to (iv) are clap along practice tracks intended to help you maintain the pulse and rhythm as you clap the rhythm patterns in these sample tests. There will be no audio tracks heard on the day of the exam. **Please check the SEC Sample Unprepared Tests in this set of exam papers.**

(viii)
Please note: SEC unprepared tests will be four bars long.
(ix)
(x)
Use these staves to compose your own sight tests
(i)
(ii)
(iii)
(iv)

Instrumental Sightreading Tests are categorised as high, medium and low register. SEC samples are included after The Practical section in this set of exam papers. SEC sight reading tests will never exceed four bars. Candidates will notify their examiner as to which register they would like to be examined in on the day

High register

Medium register

Low register

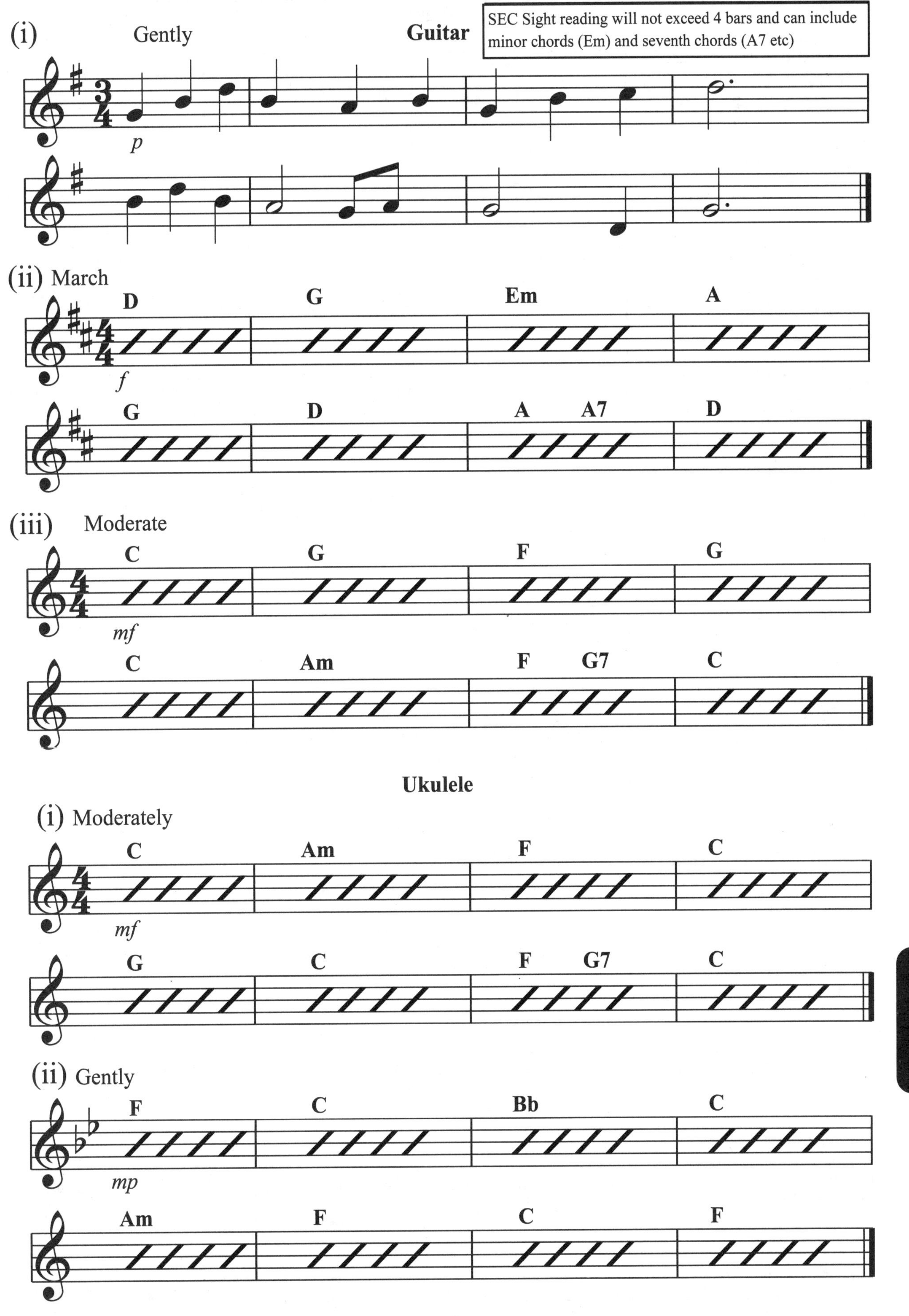
(i) Gently
Guitar
SEC Sight reading will not exceed 4 bars and can include minor chords (Em) and seventh chords (A7 etc)
p
(ii) March
D G Em A
f
G D A A7 D
(iii) Moderate
C G F G
mf
C Am F G7 C
Ukulele
(i) Moderately
C Am F C
mf
G C F G7 C
(ii) Gently
F C Bb C
mp
Am F C F

PRACTICAL
EXAM

❊ Piano
Piano
SEC Sight Tests are 4 bars only
mf
❊ Keyboard/organ
Keyboard
p
Snare Drum–Woodblock–Cajun–Bongo
(a)
f
(b)

COIMISIÚN NA SCRÚDUITHE STÁIT
STATE EXAMINATIONS COMMISSION

Junior Cycle Final Examination
Scrúdú Deiridh na Sraithe Sóisearaí

Music : Common Level
Ceol : Comhleibhéal

SAMPLE UNPREPARED TESTS
TRIALACHA SAMPLACHA gan ULLMHÚ

UNPREPARED TESTS
- **Aural Memory: Rhythm**
- **Aural memory: Melody**
- **Sight reading**
- **Improvisation**

TRIALACHA gan ULLMHÚ
- **Cluaschuimhne: Rithim**
- **Cluaschuimhne: Séis**
- **Amharcléamh**
- **Tobchumadh**

CLUASTRIALACHA CUIMHNE AURAL MEMORY TESTS
RITHIM / RHYTHM

You can find these Aural Memory Test tracks on www.examinations.ie

CLUASTRIALACHA CUIMHNE AURAL MEMORY TESTS
MELODY / SÉIS

You can find these Aural Memory Test tracks on www.examinations.ie

1

High Register / Ardréim

Medium Register / Meánréim

Low Register / Ísealréim

2

High Register / Ardréim

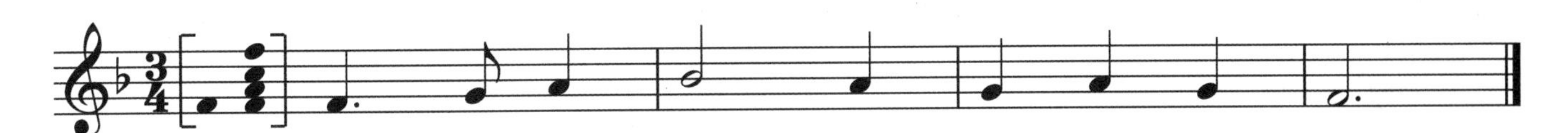

Medium Register / Meánréim

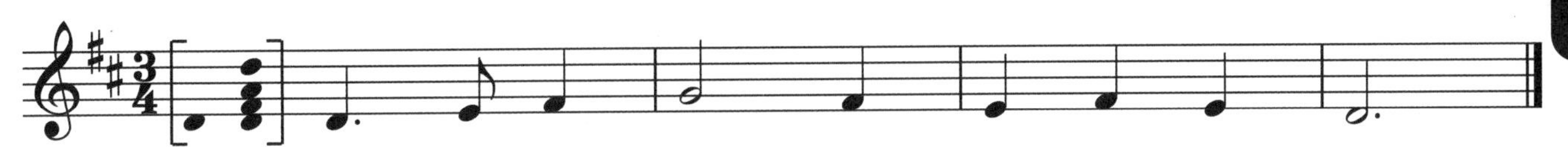

Low Register / Ísealréim

PRACTICAL EXAM

AMHARCTHRIALACHA SIGHT TESTS

1

High Register / Ardréim

Moderato

mf

Medium Register / Meánréim

Medium Register / Meánréim

Low Register / Ísealréim

2

High Register / Ardréim

Medium Register / Meánréim

Medium Register / Meánréim

Low Register / Ísealréim

PRACTICAL EXAM

AMHARCTHRIALACHA SIGHT TESTS
VOICE / GUTH

High Register / Ardréim

Medium Register / Meánréim

Low Register / Ísealréim

AMHARCTHRIALACHA SIGHT TESTS
RITHIM / RHYTHM

Classical Guitar / Giotár Clasaiceach

Rhythm Guitar / Giotár Rithimeach

1

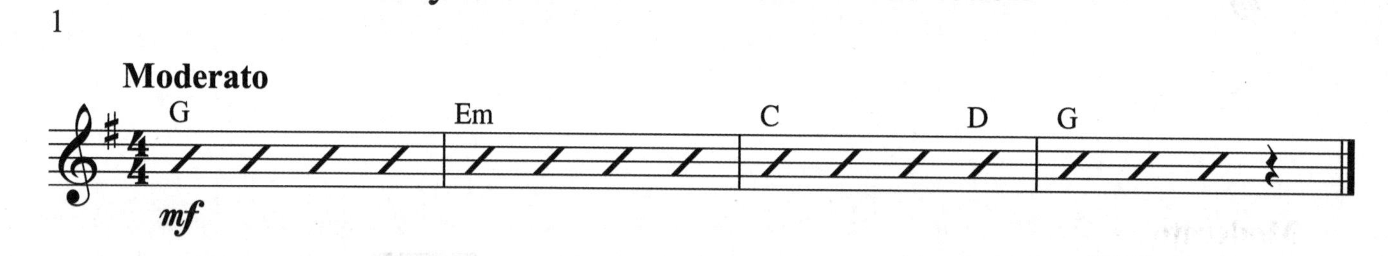

2

3

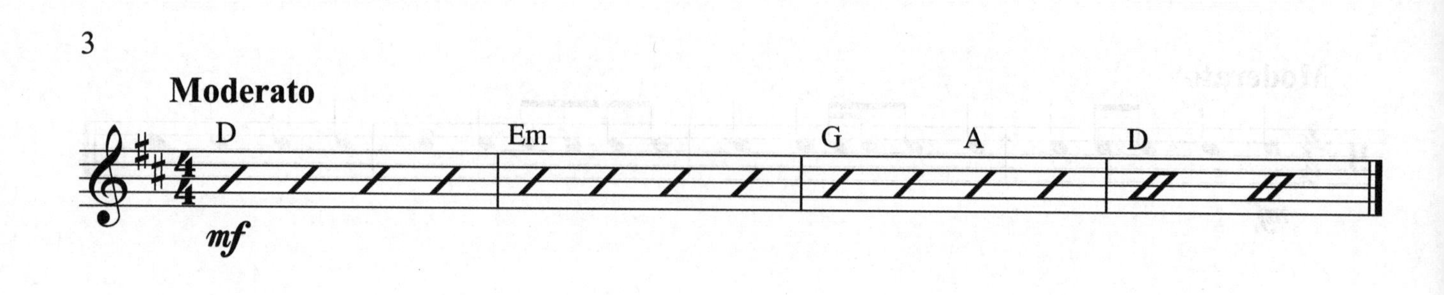

Ukulele / Ucailéile

1

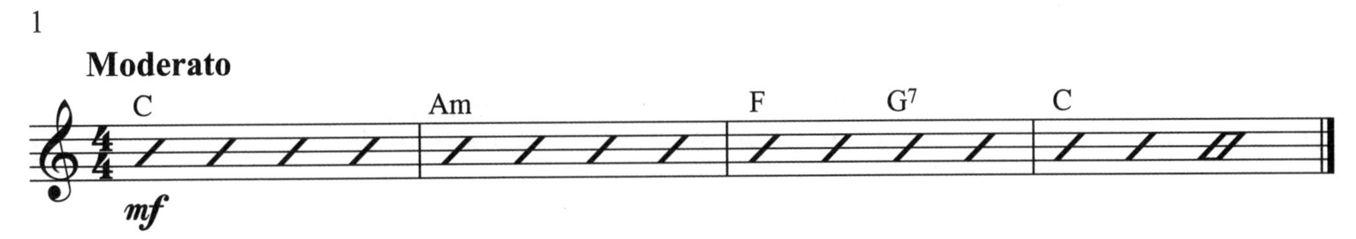

2

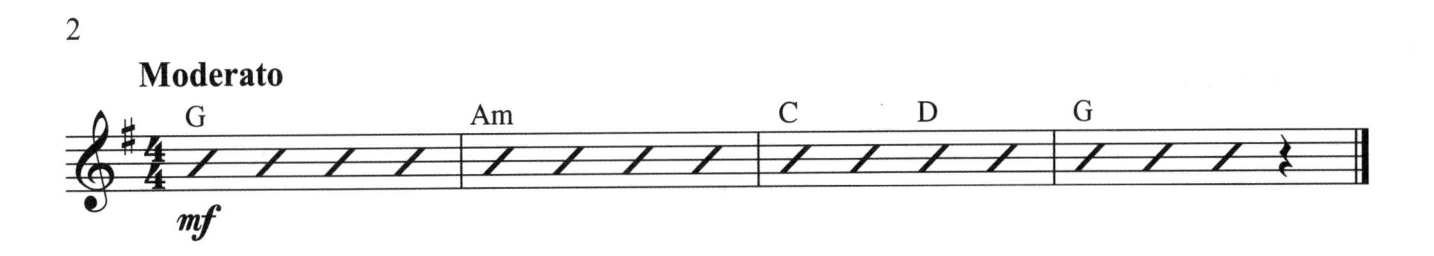

3

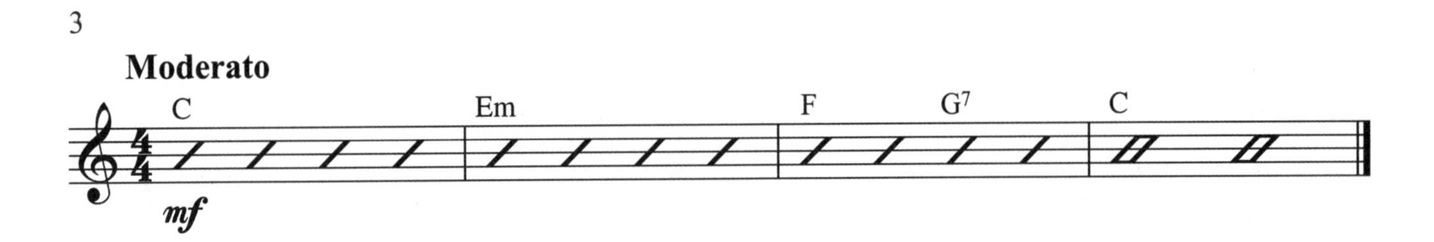

PRACTICAL EXAM

Snare-drum / Sreangdhruma

Kettle-drums / Citealdrumaí

Drum Kit / Seit Drumaí

Electronic Keyboard /Méarchlár Leictreonach

Accordion /Cairdín

Piano / Pianó

1

2

PRACTICAL EXAM

Cláirseach Cheolchoirme agus Cruit Ghaelach in C
Concert Harp and Irish Harp in C

Cláirseach Cheolchoirme agus Cruit Ghaelach in Eb
Concert Harp and Irish Harp in Eb

Cláirseach Cheolchoirme agus Cruit Ghaelach in Ab
Concert Harp and Irish Harp in Ab

Orgán / Organ

Moderato

mf

TOBCHUMADH IMPROVISATION
SÉISEACH / MELODIC

ARMÓNACH / HARMONIC

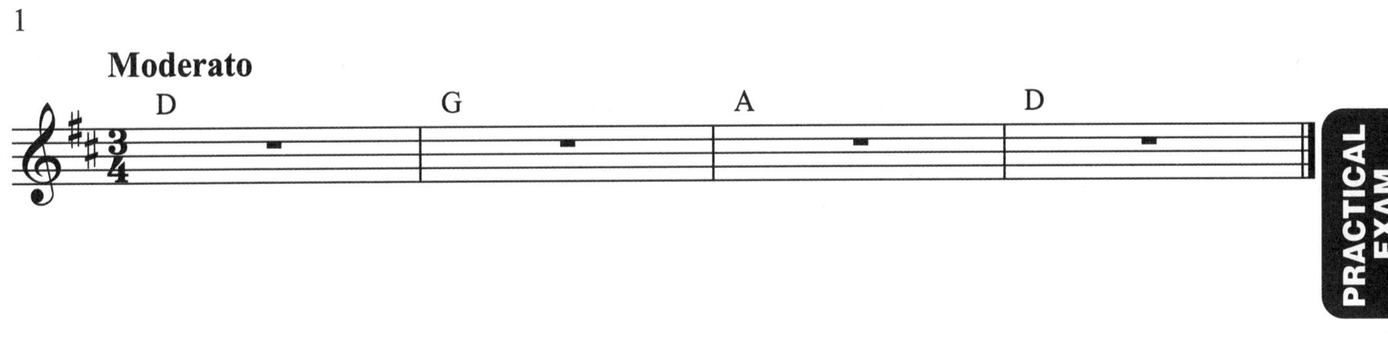

PRACTICAL EXAM

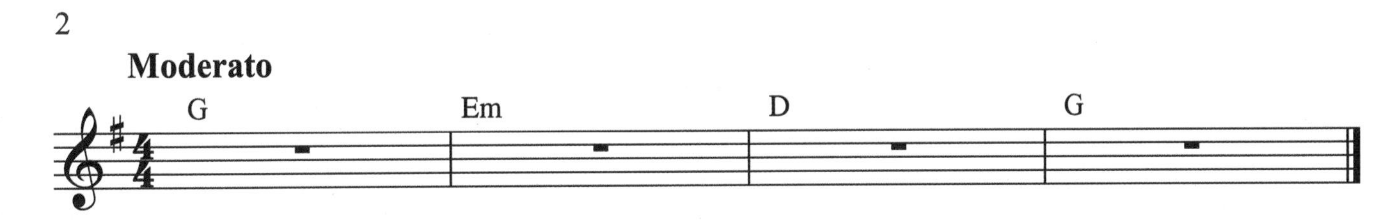

RITHIMEACH / RHYTHMIC

TOBCHUMADH AR MHODH A THUGTAR
IMPROVISATION ON A GIVEN MOOD

Tobchum ar cheann amháin díobh seo a leanas:

(i) Áthasach
(ii) Feargach
(iii) Brónach

Improvise on one of the following:

(i) Happy
(ii) Angry
(iii) Sad

Roughwork

Roughwork

Roughwork

Roughwork

Roughwork

Roughwork

Roughwork

Roughwork

//:DON'T REPLY/
KEEP THE MESSAGE/
BLOCK THE SENDER/
TELL SOMEONE YOU TRUST://

WWW.WATCHYOURSPACE.IE

Don't Accept Bullying

This Anti-Bullying campaign is supported by the Department of Education and Skills with the co-operation of the Irish Educational Publishers Association.

Edco 2022/2023 School Year Planner

SEPTEMBER	OCTOBER	NOVEMBER	DECEMBER	JANUARY	FEBRUARY	MARCH	APRIL	MAY	JUNE	JULY	AUGUST
Thurs 1	Sat 1	Tues ■ 1	Thurs 1	Sun 1	Wed ◆ 1	Wed 1	Sat 1	Mon ●◆ 1	Thurs 1	Sat ◆ 1	Tues 1
Fri 2	Sun 2	Wed ■ 2	Fri 2	Mon ● 2	Thurs 2	Thurs 2	Sun 2	Tues 2	Fri 2	Sun 2	Wed 2
Sat 3	Mon 3	Thurs ■ 3	Sat 3	Tues ■ 3	Fri 3	Fri 3	Mon ■ 3	Wed 3	Sat 3	Mon 3	Thurs 3
Sun 4	Tues 4	Fri ■ 4	Sun 4	Wed ■ 4	Sat 4	Sat 4	Tues ■ 4	Thurs 4	Sun 4	Tues 4	Fri 4
Mon 5	Wed 5	Sat ◆ 5	Mon 5	Thurs 5	Sun 5	Sun 5	Wed ■ 5	Fri 5	Mon ● 5	Wed 5	Sat 5
Tues 6	Thurs 6	Sun 6	Tues 6	Fri 6	Mon ● 6	Mon 6	Thurs ■ 6	Sat 6	Tues 6	Thurs 6	Sun 6
Wed 7	Fri 7	Mon 7	Wed 7	Sat 7	Tues 7	Tues 7	Fri ■ 7	Sun 7	Wed ◆ 7	Fri 7	Mon ● 7
Thurs 8	Sat 8	Tues 8	Thurs 8	Sun 8	Wed 8	Wed 8	Sat 8	Mon 8	Thurs 8	Sat 8	Tues 8
Fri 9	Sun 9	Wed 9	Fri 9	Mon 9	Thurs 9	Thurs 9	Sun 9	Tues 9	Fri 9	Sun 9	Wed 9
Sat 10	Mon 10	Thurs 10	Sat 10	Tues 10	Fri 10	Fri 10	Mon ● 10	Wed 10	Sat 10	Mon 10	Thurs 10
Sun 11	Tues 11	Fri 11	Sun 11	Wed 11	Sat 11	Sat 11	Tues ■ 11	Thurs 11	Sun 11	Tues 11	Fri 11
Mon 12	Wed 12	Sat 12	Mon 12	Thurs 12	Sun 12	Sun 12	Wed ■ 12	Fri 12	Mon 12	Wed 12	Sat 12
Tues 13	Thurs 13	Sun 13	Tues 13	Fri 13	Mon ■ 13	Mon 13	Thurs ■ 13	Sat 13	Tues 13	Thurs 13	Sun 13
Wed 14	Fri 14	Mon 14	Wed 14	Sat 14	Tues ■ 14	Tues 14	Fri ■ 14	Sun 14	Wed 14	Fri 14	Mon 14
Thurs 15	Sat 15	Tues 15	Thurs 15	Sun 15	Wed ■ 15	Wed 15	Sat 15	Mon 15	Thurs 15	Sat 15	Tues 15
Fri 16	Sun 16	Wed 16	Fri 16	Mon 16	Thurs ■ 16	Thurs 16	Sun 16	Tues 16	Fri 16	Sun 16	Wed 16
Sat 17	Mon 17	Thurs 17	Sat 17	Tues 17	Fri ■ 17	Fri ● 17	Mon 17	Wed 17	Sat 17	Mon 17	Thurs 17
Sun 18	Tues 18	Fri 18	Sun 18	Wed 18	Sat 18	Sat 18	Tues 18	Thurs 18	Sun 18	Tues 18	Fri 18
Mon 19	Wed 19	Sat 19	Mon 19	Thurs 19	Sun 19	Sun 19	Wed 19	Fri 19	Mon 19	Wed 19	Sat 19
Tues 20	Thurs 20	Sun 20	Tues 20	Fri 20	Mon 20	Mon 20	Thurs 20	Sat 20	Tues 20	Thurs 20	Sun 20
Wed 21	Fri 21	Mon 21	Wed 21	Sat 21	Tues 21	Tues 21	Fri 21	Sun 21	Wed 21	Fri 21	Mon 21
Thurs 22	Sat 22	Tues 22	Thurs ■ 22	Sun 22	Wed 22	Wed 22	Sat 22	Mon 22	Thurs 22	Sat 22	Tues 22
Fri 23	Sun 23	Wed 23	Fri ■ 23	Mon 23	Thurs 23	Thurs 23	Sun 23	Tues 23	Fri 23	Sun 23	Wed 23
Sat 24	Mon 24	Thurs 24	Sat 24	Tues 24	Fri 24	Fri 24	Mon 24	Wed 24	Sat 24	Mon 24	Thurs 24
Sun 25	Tues 25	Fri 25	Sun 25	Wed 25	Sat 25	Sat 25	Tues 25	Thurs 25	Sun 25	Tues 25	Fri 25
Mon 26	Wed 26	Sat 26	Mon ● 26	Thurs 26	Sun 26	Sun 26	Wed 26	Fri 26	Mon 26	Wed 26	Sat 26
Tues 27	Thurs 27	Sun 27	Tues ■ 27	Fri 27	Mon 27	Mon 27	Thurs 27	Sat 27	Tues 27	Thurs 27	Sun 27
Wed 28	Fri 28	Mon 28	Wed ■ 28	Sat 28	Tues 28	Tues 28	Fri 28	Sun 28	Wed 28	Fri 28	Mon 28
Thurs 29	Sat 29	Tues 29	Thurs ■ 29	Sun 29		Wed 29	Sat 29	Mon 29	Thurs 29	Sat 29	Tues 29
Fri 30	Sun 30	Wed 30	Fri ■ 30	Mon 30		Thurs 30	Sun 30	Tues 30	Fri 30	Sun 30	Wed 30
	Mon ● 31		Sat 31	Tues 31		Fri 31		Wed 31		Mon 31	Thurs 31

KEY DATES

● Public Holidays
■ School Holidays
◆ Important Dates

October 2022 mid-term break: All schools will close from Monday 31st October 2022 to Friday 4th November 2022 inclusive.

Christmas 2022: All schools will close on Wednesday 21st December 2022, which will be the final day of the school term. All schools will re-open on Thursday 5th January 2023.

February 2023 mid-term break: Post-Primary schools will close from Monday 13th February 2023 to Friday 17th February 2023 inclusive.

Easter 2023: All schools will close on Friday 31st March 2023, which will be the final day of the school term. All schools will re-open on Monday 17th April 2023.

5th November – CAO application facility opens for 2023 applications
1st February – Normal closing date for CAO applications
1st May – Closing date for late CAO applications
1st July – Change Your Mind CAO Deadline
The start date for the Junior & Leaving Certificate Examinations 2023 will be Wednesday 7th June.